To Shirley — Thanks for all you do! Kirsten K. 9-9-2000

Summer at the End of the World

Kirsten Kingdon

Published by
Banta & Pool, LLC
Bloomington, Indiana

International Standard Book Number:
0-9667237-1-6

Library of Congress Catalogue Card Number:
99-97143

Printed in the United States of America

For information contact:
Banta & Pool Literary Properties, LLC
1020 Greenwood Avenue
Bloomington, Indiana 47401

e-mail: writerpool@aol.com

Author's Preface

Summer at the End of the World had its unlikely beginning at an Oberlin College class reunion in May 1997. Sid Waldman, one of my husband's classmates with a talent for posing large questions and getting to the essence of a person's being, engaged me in conversation. After we'd been talking about my life for a while, he started telling me that it was fascinating and I should write a book about it. I pooh-poohed the idea until he told my husband, who responded by saying, "Well, I'm about to retire; maybe I should write it." I didn't say anything at the time, but my immediate reaction was, "Humph. I don't even like John to write my part of our Christmas letter. I'll be darned if I want him writing about my life." After we left, I promptly forgot the whole incident.

In July of that year we went vacationing in Nova Scotia in our motor home. I had never been there. While I enjoyed our whole trip, I was particularly enchanted by Cape Breton Island. Much less civilized than the rest of Nova Scotia, it offered ample opportunities for hiking and soaking up the beauty of nature.

When we reached Meat Cove at the northernmost tip of the island, I felt as though I had reached my dream place. Our first evening there we took a short hike up to a spot known as Little Grassy. As we sat there looking out over the St. Lawrence Bay, my husband said, "Maybe we can take a hike here tomorrow and not leave until late afternoon, instead of leaving in the morning as planned."

I thought for a moment and responded, "Or, alternatively, we can stay here the rest of our lives."

We couldn't do that, but we did spend four glorious days hiking and exploring the area. As we walked along the scenic and deserted trails, this book began writing itself in my head. One morning, halfway though our stay there, I woke up at 6:30 a.m. with the urge to start writing it down. Four months later I had completed my first draft.

From the beginning, the book has rested on a fictional literary device—the death of my husband. He has been remarkably good-natured about his demise in Chapter One. In general, everything that happens before that pivotal event is fact, although I have taken a few artistic liberties with details where they would have confused, rather than enlightened, the reader. Everything that comes after John's death is fictional. Derek is a totally fictional character, as are a few other minor characters, and most names have been changed.

People have asked me why I added these fictional elements. In one sense, I cannot provide a satisfactory answer to that question. I wrote the story as it came to me. Upon reflection, however, I see that this approach gave me a reason to look back on my life. The relationship between my husband and me—the central relationship of my adult life—was easier to portray by imagining life without John. Taking that path also allowed me to add the relationship between Jim and Derek, which proves to be so pivotal in my imagined healing process.

I have borrowed some key elements of the story from friends. The reaction of Derek's family to learning that he is gay is essentially that of Lani and Robert Graves. I was powerfully moved by their story when it was published in the Metro DC newsletter, the *Flagpole*. The quote from Derek's mother is, in fact, a quote from Lani. I thank them for letting me use their story and hasten to add that the family details, including where they live and, especially, Derek's mother's death, are all totally fictitious. Derek's story of his travails regarding his doctoral dissertation is also pure fiction, as is its content, and everything else about him.

The other borrowed element is the sermon at the end of the book. It is one I heard preached by Michael Lindvall, senior pastor at First Presbyterian Church in Ann Arbor, Michigan, the fall I was writing the book. I thank him for his generosity in giving me a copy and permission to use it in a work of fiction.

Some liberties have also been taken with the setting of the story. Meat Cove has been renamed Bear Cove. The origin of Meat Cove is a story in itself which I thought would distract from mine. The Co-op store has been relocated to Cape North to be closer to the Museum, which is located there. I do not know what Pollett Cove or the trail going through it are like as, alas, I still have not hiked it. The same is true of Money Point and its trail. Unfortunately, the cabin exists only in my imagination. I am deliberately vague about the location of the airport where Greta lands, as I suspect the itinerary I lay out for that day is unrealistic. I have replaced the Cape St. Lawrence Light, a rather utilitarian and prosaic structure, with an old-fashioned lighthouse much like the famous lighthouse at Peggy's Cove. Other details may be wrong due to the inadequacies of my memory.

Similarly, accounts of what happened the summer in which this story is set are fictional as well. Thus I am deliberately vague about what supposedly happened that summer at the Presbyterian General Assembly, although the historical details are as accurate as my memory. In another example, details of Washington, D.C., that summer may ring false to readers familiar with the city and its recent history as some of them are totally made up.

Since writing this book, I have had a career change. I am no longer a practicing attorney as I was when I wrote this (my retirement also being fictional), but am the Executive Director of the national Parents, Families and Friends of Lesbians and Gays (PFLAG), which plays a part in the story. While my history, as recounted in this book, certainly is germane to my present job, it is important to emphasize that this book expresses my own experience and beliefs, and does not reflect those of PFLAG as an organization.

Writing this book has been enormously satisfying, and I can only hope that my readers enjoy reading it as much as I have enjoyed writing it.

Washington, D.C.
October 1999

Acknowledgements

My deepest appreciation goes to my family. My husband cheerfully allowed himself to die a tragically premature death for the sake of the story, as well as reading and rereading my manuscript, advising me at every turn, and putting up with my preoccupation as I worked out details in my head and on paper. Our son Jim allowed, and even encouraged, me to take the liberty of using him as a character. He and his brother Tor both advised me as I explored with them what kind of partner would suit Jim. It will not surprise readers of this book to learn that we all concluded that the nature of the relationship is paramount. My daughter, my sisters, and my brother all were helpful and supportive. I could not have written such a personal book without all of these people, partly because of their help and partly because of their steadfast love and friendship.

Many friends have read the manuscript and given me the assurance I needed to believe that it was a publishable work. I am especially indebted to my early readers and those who have provided useful and valuable editing suggestions, among them Susan Javens, Louise Buchanan, Jeanne Talpers, Nancy Davidson, Jodi Kingdon, Robert Kingdon and David Dudley. David, my husband's nephew, deserves special mention for taking my dream of simple pen and ink drawings and making it a reality far exceeding my vision.

Even with all this, it is my editor and publisher, Gary Pool, who believed in me, inspired me and instructed me in such a way that my manuscript, somewhat to my amazement, became a book. With consummate skill, patience and understanding he challenged me to achieve more than I would have thought possible. Working with him and with his business partner, Frank Banta, has been an unalloyed pleasure. A special note of appreciation goes to Rhea Murray, without whose book, *A Journey to Moriah,* I never would have met Gary. Rhea is a very special woman and it is a privilege to share an editor and publisher with her.

Dedication

To my very much alive and well husband, John

SUMMER AT THE END OF THE WORLD

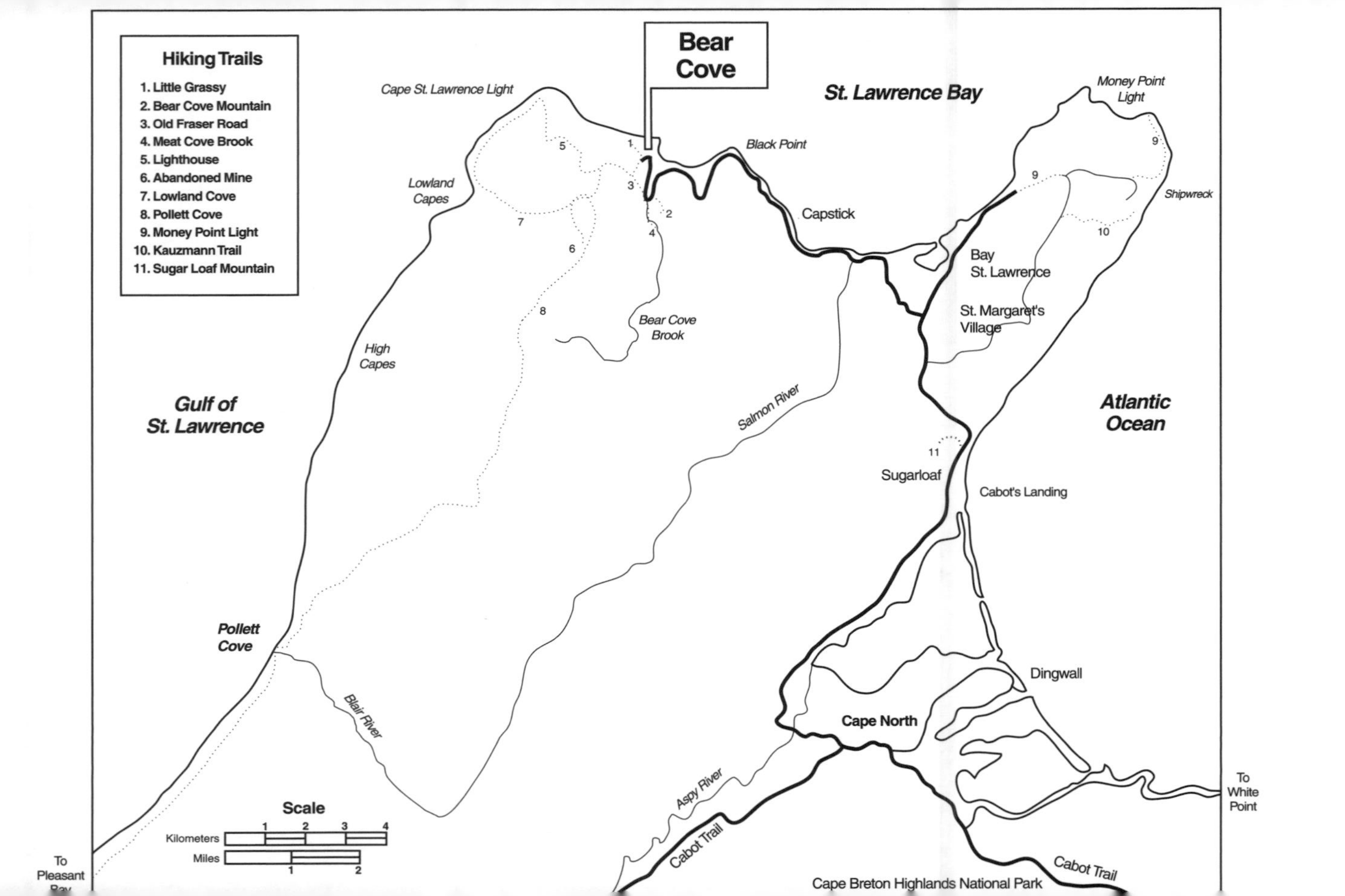
Bear
Cove
Hiking Trails
1. Little Grassy
2. Bear Cove Mountain
3. Old Fraser Road
4. Meat Cove Brook
5. Lighthouse
6. Abandoned Mine
7. Lowland Cove
8. Pollett Cove
9. Money Point Light
10. Kauzmann Trail
11. Sugar Loaf Mountain
Cape St. Lawrence Light
St. Lawrence Bay
Money Point Light
Black Point
Lowland Capes
Capstick
Shipwreck
Bay St. Lawrence
St. Margaret's Village
Bear Cove Brook
High Capes
Gulf of St. Lawrence
Salmon River
Atlantic Ocean
Sugarloaf
Cabot's Landing
Pollett Cove
Blair River
Dingwall
Cape North
Aspy River
Scale
Kilometers
Miles
Cabot Trail
To White Point
To Pleasant Bay
Cape Breton Highlands National Park
Cabot Trail

Prologue

I came to think of it as my cabin at the end of the world. It wasn't really either, of course. I was lucky to find it when I needed it, but it wasn't mine and it wasn't at the end of the world. There was plenty of Canada north of it—Newfoundland, for instance. And I'd been farther north, certainly, when I had visited Norway.

But it felt like the end of the world. If it wasn't on the very northernmost tip of Nova Scotia, it was close to it. The only things you could see on the horizon were the tiny, uninhabited island of St. Paul and occasional ocean-going vessels slowly moving out of sight. They looked like cut-out figures in a kid's play and moved without noise or visible means of propulsion other than an occasional faint smudge of smoke.

And I had fled to it, gratefully, when it felt as though my world were ending. When I didn't know how I could go on living, or even if I wanted to, without my best friend, lover and husband. When all our plans for what we would do with our brand-new retirements disappeared the day he died like the smoke from the ships. When I was still numb and uncertain of who I was without him. When the memorial service was over, family, friends and neighbors went back to their own lives, and the immediate financial decisions had been made. When I couldn't stand being in the apartment where every inch of space reminded me of him and of our life together. When my life felt like a play written by someone else, for someone else, and I felt miscast. I knew I was in trouble when I didn't even want to go to church, visit friends, bike the Capital Crescent trail, or walk in the zoo. I was so heavy-hearted that I felt as though I would turn into stone if I didn't do something drastic. And so, for the first time in my life I fled the apartment I had loved and Washington, D.C., the city I had adopted as mine six years earlier.

How lucky I was to find a cabin in the very place we had last vacationed together. A place where we had sweet times together, but a place with plenty of room to explore. To explore the area, but also to explore those urgent questions within me. Without John, who was I? With his death I had begun to realize, painfully, that more of my identity than I cared to acknowledge was tied up with being John's wife, and with our shared identity. Where did I go from here? Was this the end of my world of happiness and fulfillment or could I, like my mother in her years of widowhood, make a new life for myself with different joys and sorrows than I had known in my thirty-three years of marriage? And, even if I could, how could I get to the point where I actually had the will and energy to start this next phase of my life?

Chapter 1

Setting Sail

I awoke slowly to the sound of spring-time birds and the welcome sight of sunshine pouring in the window. I couldn't see any breeze in the trees yet, but the clock at my bedside registered 8:02. It was still early.

Rolling over, I saw John's eyelids twitch in his sleep. He was either waking up or dreaming. I surveyed him with contentment, and cheerfully contemplated the day ahead—and the days and months and years to follow. We'd been married almost thirty-three years, and life had never looked sweeter. Reaching over, I gently smoothed his bushy eyebrows and stroked his almost completely white beard. Almost automatically, and seemingly in his sleep, he moved his head and kissed my fingers. His eyes opened languorously and he smiled at me. Putting his right arm around me, he pulled me close. Adjusting my pillow, I moved into our "classic snuggle" position, legs entangled, cradled in his arm, cheek against his shoulder.

"Looks like a beautiful day," I murmured. Only then did his eyes move to the window.

"Hmm. Could be a beautiful sailing day," he responded.

"I thought so." Happily, I thought of our trim, twenty-eight-foot sailboat fresh from its winter's storage, newly painted and carpeted, and just waiting for the first good sailing day. The smell of the briny Chesapeake Bay, the sight of sunlight sparkling on the blue-green waves, the fun of days spent on the water with family and friends beckoned.

"Maybe I should check on the forecast." That was my signal to untangle myself and roll out of bed. I handed John his weather radio and headed to the bathroom. When I got back, he was seated in the bedroom recliner listening intently to one of the three or four predictions he would check. I padded over to the hall door, retrieved the newspaper and checked its forecast, which looked very promising: sunny all day, high in the lower 70s, winds on the bay 10 to 15 knots. I took the paper in to John and went to fix oatmeal for the two of us. It looked like a great day for sailing.

"It sounds like perfect sailing weather," John reported as he came into the kitchen. "Should we try Marge and Joe and see if they are free?" I'd met Marge when she and I were brand-new students at the University of Michigan Law School. We were not quite the average students, having both just turned forty. Successful careers lay behind us as well as ahead of us. We became the nucleus of what we referred to as the "geriatric study group," and had become close friends. She and her husband owned a house on what was locally referred to as "the creek," although I always thought of it as a widening of one of the rivers feeding the bay. By land their house was not far from the marina where our boat was. By boat it was a pleasant day's excursion.

"What a first-rate idea!" I responded. We hadn't seen them since John retired from teaching at the University of Michigan and I wound up my law practice. It would be fun to compare notes. Joe has retired several times although Marge is still hard at work as in-house counsel for a professional association.

John reported back, just as I was dishing up breakfast, that they were busy in the morning, but would be at home in the afternoon. They would love to have us sail over, join them for supper and a game of bridge, stay overnight and then sail back with us on Sunday to our marina.

"Splendid," I said, smiling at John, holding my face up for a kiss, which he returned so passionately that it threatened to derail our plans. We were both thoroughly enjoying this phase of our lives together. We were young enough to be healthy and vigorous and still old enough to have gained some wisdom, and some money, and to appreciate having time free to play. Most importantly, we felt lucky to be married and in love. Unencumbered by dependents, work responsibilities, or a house, we were free to follow our hearts where they led.

But this morning the hot oatmeal and beckoning breezes were enough to bring us back to practical details, although the sexual electricity remained between us as we packed up to go.

Just as I was putting in a few last things, John saw a pair of stray socks that had gotten mixed up in our laundry. "Why don't I drop these off in the laundry room, and meet you at the car?"

"OK. I'll be down there by the time you are."

"Don't forget to bolt the door as you leave."

"I won't," I promised, smiling inwardly. I was fifty-six years old, an accomplished attorney, had frequently been alone in the apartment, and have never failed to bolt the door when I left. Still, John always reminded me. I used to get angry at him, and felt that he was challenging my competence. By now I had learned that it was just the way he was and took it as a sign of affection. If he didn't love me and trust me, he would wait for me and bolt the door himself.

I was a little surprised that I reached the car before he did, but thought that maybe he had run into a neighbor and gotten into a conversation. Besides, the elevator on that side of our condominium was notoriously slow. So I put our things in the car and headed off toward the laundry room.

As I turned the corner, I saw what at first looked like a dropped load of laundry. In shock, I realized that it was John, lying inert on the floor. I rushed to him, and only as I was running did I realize that I was screaming. As I reached him, our closest neighbors, Paul and Darryl, who were just coming in the back door, joined me. In a panic, I knelt down and cradled John's head in my arms. I could detect no signs of life and couldn't stop screaming, crying, sobbing and kissing him all at once.

Paul gently pushed me aside, checked for a pulse and started artificial respiration. Darryl went dashing off to call an ambulance.

It seemed like forever until the ambulance and paramedics came with a stretcher, but it couldn't have been more than a few minutes. One of the paramedics brushed Paul aside, checked for a pulse, asked how long he'd been like this, and began artificial respiration himself. I'd stopped screaming, but was still sobbing and holding on to John, and couldn't seem to speak. Paul answered in a tense, urgent, but calm voice, "We just found him. We called immediately."

Somehow I could respond to Paul even though I couldn't seem to comprehend the questions the paramedic was yelling at me.

"What hospital?" Paul asked with concern. My mind whirled. We'd just been talking about that. What had John said?

"Georgetown." I finally was able to grasp a coherent thought and spit it out.

"Who's his doctor?"

"Stewart Olson." That one was a little easier.

"They won't let us go in the ambulance. We'll follow you in our car and see you in the ER." Their faces swam in my teary vision as I automatically followed the stretcher into the ambulance, my hands clutching John's hands, his sweatshirt, whatever I could cling to.

The siren blaring, we sped down Connecticut Avenue. The paramedics switched places and the second one took over the artificial respiration. John's face was ashen, though, and he showed no signs of life. The paramedics looked resigned. I still sobbed, but now I was addressing God: "Please, please, he can't be dead. No, God, no, please, please." I was panic-stricken at the thought of life without him, and clung to hope.

As we arrived at the hospital, we were met by a team of physicians with equipment. They moved in around John, pushing me out of the way. No one said anything except for a few barked commands which made no sense to me. I was quiet, nourishing the hope that, now all these doctors were here, everything would be all right. But, all too soon, their frantic activities stopped and one of the doctors looked up at me, mumbled, "Sorry," quickly turned away and crisply said to someone in a white coat holding a clipboard, "DOA; unable to resuscitate." The words reverberated in my head: "DOA." Dead on arrival. "Unable to resuscitate." In that crowded and busy room, I suddenly felt terribly alone.

Almost instantly, Darryl and Paul appeared. Relieved beyond words by their presence, I burst into tears again when I tried to tell them what the doctor had said. I still couldn't believe that this was actually happening. It began to sink in more when John's doctor sat me down, sat next to me and gently explained that, in spite of the fact that John was only fifty-seven years old and apparently in the best of health, he had had a massive stroke, and died instantly. There was no way it could have been predicted and no way he knew of that it could have been prevented. Even if I had been with him when it happened, there wasn't anything I could have done. He hadn't suffered.

I don't know how I got through that day which started so happily and ended as a nightmare. I don't think I could have done it without Paul and Darryl. They called our son Jim and took me back to their apartment, picking Jim up on the way, and helped me tell him. Together we all called Tor, our younger son, who was living on the west coast. I managed to call Stephanie, my daughter, and Marge and Joe. Gradually the practical questions numbed my grief and pain, at least for the moment, leaving me like a zombie, moving on automatic pilot with no feelings.

Chapter 2

The Co-op General Store

Planning the memorial service kept me occupied. Family and friends came and went. I hugged them, cried, answered questions. I was grateful that people guided me; I seemed to be incapable of initiating anything. Neighbors put up out-of-town arrivals, food arrived, dishes were washed.

My pastor ministered to me. He read me psalms, and prayed with me. I was grateful, because I was too numb to pray—something I'd never thought would happen. He asked questions of all of us. Based on what we told him and on what he knew of John, he fashioned a remembrance of John, every word of which was evocative of the man who was my husband and who was now lost to me for all my days on this earth. Afterwards, I was surrounded by a sea of people sharing my loss. We comforted each other, but my heart was so bleak I could hardly say or comprehend anything.

Gradually over the course of the next week people left until I was alone in the apartment. Our apartment. Memories of the past haunted me like ghosts in the room. I'd lie awake, torturing myself with memories. I'd finally get up, drink some warm milk, fall asleep over a book in the recliner, only to wake up again when I moved to my bed. I went over every memory of that last morning. I was tormented by the thought that I could have done something differently which would have kept John alive, even while my brain knew that was sheer nonsense. We should have made love. I should have gone with him to take the socks back. I never should have left him for a minute.

By day I knew that I was trying to preserve some kind of illusion that I could have controlled something that was totally out of my control. At night, however, the thoughts returned.

I tried watching television, but found myself watching only John's favorite shows and wishing he were there. Music was worse. Every CD I played reminded me of the times we'd listened to it together. The very tones of the voices on the National Public Radio news shows reminded me of how John used to have those shows on in every room he entered.

Friends invited me over, but I could hardly stand inflicting myself on them. I felt like a wet blanket, bringing with me my own private cloud of gloom. Even when I spent time with Jim, I felt that I was just intensifying his grief instead of helping either of us to move beyond the huge gaping hole left by John's death. I found myself spending more and more time alone in the apartment—I couldn't stand either to think of it as "our apartment" or as "my apartment."

Finally, I couldn't bear it any more. In desperation I remembered how I'd been captivated by Cape Breton Island where we'd spent our last vacation together. Rooting through our memorabilia from that trip, I found the number of the campground where we'd stayed. Miraculously, they knew of a cabin tucked away in the woods above them. I couldn't believe my luck when I found out that it was available for the whole summer.

*

* *

On the last leg of the long drive up to the northernmost tip of Nova Scotia, I stop at the Co-op General Store in Cape North, at the turnoff for the cove, to get some basics. Although I have already stocked up, I can't pass it by. It reminds me of my father's passionate support for cooperatives, and triggers a wave of memories so intense that I feel as though Dad is in the car with me.

My father was tall, broad-shouldered, warm, unpredictable, Norwegian to his core. He was intellectually curious, a fighter for justice, a talker, a doer, infuriatingly stubborn.

As a child I adored him. He kept a fire burning in our big fireplace almost all winter and especially when guests arrived. I never could figure out how he could go out into the snowy Wisconsin winter to replenish the supply of logs without losing a beat in the conversation. He'd see that everyone had drinks, he'd bring out the herring or the smoked fish and sometimes, long after Mother had gone to bed, he would lead a raid on the refrigerator. And how he would talk!

The talk was always interesting when Dad was around. With my Uncle Chet it was usually about politics. Each of them sounded as though he were starved for a kindred soul, and, as I look back on it, they probably were. Neither my mother nor my Aunt Bernice was especially interested in politics in those years filled with child-rearing and making ends meet, and there weren't many in our conservative area of the country who could agree with these two free-thinkers.

My Uncle Chet was the kind of Christian who would ask himself, when faced with a decision, "What would Jesus do?" And then he'd do it. When World War II came, and he was a young man of draft age, he couldn't rid himself of the conviction that Jesus wouldn't sign up to kill other young men, no matter how misguided and even evil their leaders were. Hadn't Jesus refused to lead a rebellion against the Romans?

At the time Chet was married and had two young children. If he refused to serve, he stood a real chance of being arrested or, at least, losing his job. His younger brother was itching to reach the age where he could enlist. Despite this, Chet became one of the few conscientious objectors. His decision made him pretty unpopular with the men in the paper mill where he worked. They had brothers and sons who were risking their lives in the war Chet refused to fight. Many of them thought he was a coward and a traitor. But Chet persevered and, somewhat to his surprise, was neither jailed nor fired.

My father didn't have to face that issue. He was legally blind, so the armed services didn't want him, even if he had wanted to serve. Like Chet, however, my father didn't hesitate to voice his convictions even when they were unpopular. He was regarded with suspicion by his fellow mill workers. He was a Norwegian immigrant with an accent that sounded German to many of them. A democratic socialist, in the European sense, he was an odd duck politically to these fiercely anti-Communist sons and grandsons of Polish immigrants. They could never forget that their homeland had now been taken over by the Russian Communists. Even Dad's activities as a union organizer didn't erase his coworkers' suspicions of his politics.

So it wasn't too surprising that these two strong men, who were willing to pay the social price for their convictions and to stand alone, would become fast friends and allies. They were both well read, stubborn, intellectual, sure of themselves and articulate. No wonder I loved to sit in on their discussions. When they disagreed, neither would give an inch. Even when they agreed, it was with a vehemence that might have led a casual observer to think they were disagreeing.

They were quite a pair. Dad, who read with difficulty, needing ever stronger magnifying glasses, was a large, gentle, big-hearted man who was slow to anger. Never much of a church-goer, he still was an admirer of Jesus and his message of social responsibility. He was always a spokesman for the underdog. His voice, bearing the marks of his native Norway, was deliberate but passionate, deep and usually calm. He was without a competitive bone in his body, and almost always had a beer at his side. Chet, on the other hand, was quick, slight of build and volatile in mood. The grandson of Norwegian immigrants, he was an engineer who became a manager and a part-time farmer. Although a pacifist, he was also a deer-hunter, and a vocal and tenacious competitor at cards, croquet and debate. An active Methodist, he was so ascetic that he didn't even drink coffee.

As a child I took their relationship for granted. It was only as an adult that I came to appreciate how lucky Dad was, with his own brother and sisters in Norway, to have Chet for a brother-in-law. It was easy to understand why Dad agreed to move to Neenah-Menasha in 1943, almost on a whim, when Chet urged my parents to do so and even found them a house they could afford.

Over the years Chet and Dad became more than brothers-in-law and friends. They became allies, and leaders in bringing a cooperative grocery store and gas station to Neenah, Wisconsin. Dad knew co-ops from Norway. His fiercely egalitarian sense of justice was perfectly in tune with this movement. He believed in having enterprises owned by the users and workers.

Early in life, I recognized that these two men had a commitment to justice which was rare. Their passion spoke to something deep inside me. My heroes were Martin Luther King, Jr., and Gandhi. I loved to read of the early Christian martyrs and of people who risked all to do what was right. In my daydreams I faced crises of conscience and imagined myself standing up for truth and right no matter what the cost. In my heart I feared that I would not be equal to the task.

John was a counterpoint to that side of my nature. He shared my father's intellectual curiosity, but not the same passion for equality. John and I almost always agreed on what was right and fair, and he supported many of the causes I believe in, but he wasn't a fighter in the same sense that Dad and Chet were. John was more sensible than I am, and I realize with a stab of pain how much I am going to miss that. His calm, balanced perspective wasn't something that came naturally to me. I had learned in marriage that I reached better decisions—whether the subject was child-rearing or fighting unfairness—when I bounced my ideas off John and listened to his reactions.

Were the roots of my father's intensity his own feelings of inferiority? I know he felt he never should have been born because his arrival made his recently widowed mother's life too difficult. Or was it just that he, having been born shortly after his father was killed in a freak accident, and being raised as a fatherless child, could empathize with those who had less than others? As an adult I can still feel frustrated as I contrast his apparent ability to empathize with strangers with his inability to do so with his own children.

He had come to Wisconsin to work on his uncle's mink farm as a 19-year-old unable to find employment in Norway. Only as I have raised children of my own have I come to realize how pathetically young that is to be leaving your entire known family. But the depression hit in Norway before it hit this country, and his family was poor. He planned to earn enough money to return to Norway in three years. But he didn't stay with his uncle the full three years. Although he never told us why he left, we could read between the lines. We suspected that he was not treated well by his uncle. All he ever said about him was that he drank and he didn't treat his dog well. Knowing how gentle and caring my father was with animals, that simple statement spoke volumes to us.

As a young immigrant in Milwaukee with a degree in business from Norway, which did not impress anyone here, and with the depression having shrunk job opportunities to practically nothing, he was lucky to get work in a plumbing store. Big and strong, with a willingness to work, he never lacked employment despite his youth, his foreign accent and his eyesight. But the jobs he could get were not jobs that used his considerable intellect or his desire to help society.

For intellectual companionship and challenge, and to feel he was helping society, he became involved in a wide variety of causes. During World War II he befriended the Japanese-Americans who were detained in a "relocation center" near Provo, Utah, where we lived briefly. After we moved back to Wisconsin, he and Chet started the Co-op. Dad helped organize the workers in the paper mill where he worked, and he supported the refugees from Latvia who moved to our area after the War. World peace was an abiding passion of his. All of his causes fit under the general category of working to achieve a more just and humane world.

Many of the good anti-Communist Polish-Americans in our town saw Dad as a Communist, pure and simple. At one point he was defeated for PTA president because of that. He was a person who swam against the stream in that provincial, conservative, small town only a few miles from the home of Joe McCarthy, notorious Red-baiting Senator in the years of my youth. But the disapproval of many of his fellow citizens did not deter him.

In other ways, too, he probably scandalized our neighbors. In a devoutly Catholic community, he belonged to what was called "The Liberal Religious Fellowship Group." I seem to recall that it had some vaguely Unitarian affiliation, but mostly, as I saw it as a teenager, it was a group of people who cared as much about social justice as my father did. I remember attending one Sunday morning meeting when the topic was the plight of American Indians on the nearby reservations. If God was mentioned, I do not recall it.

Dad made no bones about the fact that, at the age of seventeen, he had surveyed the world's religions and found them all wanting, a conclusion he never found reason to change. His serene dismissal of religion frustrated and puzzled my mother, who was as devout as he was unreligious.

As I came to understand his feelings better over the years, however, I realized they were not quite as simple as he said they were. I remember his story about how he and his best friend would talk about the power that created the world. In telling this, Dad would grimace, and grab his head between his hands in a reenactment of their childish sense of awe: "Don't even think about it," they would warn each other, "or your head will burst!"

He believed this great power that had created the world had, in some inexplicable way, created it so that following the Golden Rule worked. Strange as it might seem to human reason, loving your enemies reaps benefits to the person doing so, regardless of the effect on the enemy. Those who ignore the Golden Rule, who operate out of greed or hatred, no matter how they *appear* to prosper, in the final analysis, do not. Dad was a great admirer of Gandhi, of Martin Luther King, Jr., and of the nonviolent tactics they used, which, as he saw it, were outgrowths of the teachings of Jesus.

Dad was, in many ways, a profoundly good man. But the part he never could accept about Christianity is that a God so great He could create the world, and create it so that moral goodness was rewarded, could care about him.

Once, when our sons Jim and Tor were young, I visited my parents at a time when John could not join us. During that visit Dad and I took Jim and Tor to Green Bay to visit a newly opened train museum. The boys were enchanted and we all had a good time, or so I thought until we got back to Menasha that night. After the boys were put to bed, and Mother, Dad and I were sitting around talking, it became clear that Dad had been deeply hurt by the fact that I had paid so much attention to Jim and Tor and so little to him. Stunned into silence, I realized that Dad was jealous of his own grandchildren. That was the first time I was able to see my strong and capable father as someone who felt so needy he begrudged the attention his daughter gave her young children. Only then did I fully realize the scars that his childhood had left on him.

In thinking about this insight in later years, I began to see the connection between Dad's sense of inadequacy and his inability to feel that a God mighty enough to create the universe could care about him. It always made me sad, but I knew that no words from any of us could change his deep-seated feelings of unworthiness or could make him realize God loves all of us, and maybe even especially the unworthy. I came to think of Dad as someone who took on all of the burdens of Christianity without the benefits that come with knowing God loves you and will be with you through all life's troubles.

I loved Dad's zealous concern for all those in need or who had been treated unjustly. As a child, however, I adored him more for the fun we had together. He bought a canoe and taught us how to use it. This opened up a whole new dimension to our world. How we loved to take off from our back yard in the canoe to explore the lake on which our house stood. Although from the road our house showed its humble origins as a summer cabin and looked unpromising, from the lake it appeared cozy as it sat among the trees at the crest of an expansive and rolling lawn.

In the winter Dad took us ice skating on the lake, testing the ice with a long, pointed, iron rod. When we travelled, he piqued our curiosity with his questions. His poor eyesight meant he had to rely on us to tell him the names of towns, of their large factories, of their physical features. He talked of far-off Norway with an appreciation that made it seem almost like paradise. And his laugh was impossible to resist.

I also feared my father. When angry, he was scary. My earliest memory is of the pain and sheer terror of being spanked by him, knowing that he was out of control. I learned diplomacy as a way to avoid evoking his rage.

But, in spite of my fear, I knew he loved me deeply. I still have pictures of him playing with me when I was a baby. One memorable picture shows him sitting in my playpen in our back yard while I tried to get in. I remember how, in later years, he would come in, see me lying on the floor reading a book, usually in front of the fireplace, and affectionately tousle my hair and turn on a light. He delighted in my love of reading. He'd always wanted a "bookworm" for a child, and I, his first-born, certainly fulfilled that wish.

He taught me much. When I was in high school, he served as editor and coach encouraging, inspiring, correcting me as I worked on an essay for a Boeing "People to People" scholarship. His thorough review, his thoughtful questions and comments, his gentle, but rigorous, corrections far exceeded anything I had received in school. The $500 I won for that essay was a lot of money in those days. The habits of hard work and careful writing that had been drilled into him in Norway remained with him. He was an excellent writer, even though his perfectionism and self-criticism kept his output low.

I also inherited much from my father. I can see his influence in my intellectual curiosity, my love of adventure, and my quest to explore new territory, both intellectually and geographically. Only last Christmas, my son Jim and I traced the genealogical distribution of this love of exploring. We tromped through the woods, over rivers and, finally, along the Potomac in the winter darkness, walking from Turkey Run Park to the Rosslyn Metro station. As it got late and darkness began to fall, we knew we should stop along the way and call for a ride from John and Tor, the nonhikers. We demonstrated our inheritance as we let our curiosity prevail.

Dad was the first big loss of my adult life. He was diagnosed with a fatal and inoperable brain tumor almost fifteen years ago. I was in his hospital room, along with Mother, when his doctor told him. We cried together. That in itself was extraordinary. I had never seen my father cry before. Mother told me later she had seen him cry only once before. That was on their honeymoon when he heard Germany had invaded Norway.

But within minutes, to our astonishment, Dad was smiling and then even laughing as he thought about the reactions of one of his favorite co-workers, Shep, with whom he used to have long and heated arguments about religion. He imagined telling Shep he was sorry he was dying, because he had really wanted to go someplace warm that winter. Someplace like Florida or Italy. Shep's reply, he was sure, would be: "Well, Ebbe, I don't think you have to worry. You're going to go someplace a lot hotter a lot sooner!"

Dad's final days were a time I will always remember. We brought him home from the hospital. Together we called Norway to tell his brother—less than two years older—that he was dying. We were there as family and friends gathered to share the grief and joy of his last few months. All of us drove to Menasha for Christmas through frigid winter weather with wind chill readings of minus 70 degrees. Dad uncharacteristically fretted about our safety, but we all came, serene in the certainty that nothing could keep us from sharing this last Christmas together.

Recently I came across a letter my father had written to his family in Norway about that last Christmas:

> This will be my last Christmas letter and I feel such a need to thank you all for all the happy years that we have shared. These last days—strange as it may seem—have really also been full of happiness. The family have gathered around and we have been very close and loving and I think that we have appreciated having this opportunity to be so close. So it has not been all sadness but also much rich experience. I've been having excellent care because all the children and grandchildren have traveled long distances on snowy roads to be with me.
>
> So far I've had no pain and my mind has been clear. I've never thought much about life after death, but I must admit that thoughts of it are becoming more tempting.
>
> I have such wonderful family on both sides of the ocean and I do hope that you will continue to keep in touch with each other.

The letter is typed, probably by Mother at his dictation, and signed with his characteristic large, legible script whose shakiness betrays the tumor eating away at his spatial sense.

After Christmas Mother, with amazing courage and faith, went with him to Norway for a final visit to his many relatives, not even knowing whether he would be able to make the trip back. They visited us in Ann Arbor after they returned. I remember waiting to see them come out of the plane and the stab of pain I felt when I saw the attendants carry my usually strong and stalwart father down the stairs in a chair. After they returned to Menasha, the four of us children took turns coming home to help Mother and to be with him. During that time, I knew, as I never had before, what it was to feel cradled by God's love.

Now I remember with envy our time grieving together as a family before Dad died. I had no opportunity for that with John.

After Dad's death I suffered the most when I knew I would never again, on this earth, hear his laugh or his unanticipated reaction to world events, never sit around the fire talking with him, and never again experience being his beloved oldest daughter. I didn't experience the same all-consuming loss I do as a widow. But I do remember feeling a distance from the world of the living after my father's memorial service. After being immersed in the intensity associated with knowing you have very little time together remaining, the daily questions I faced after his death seemed unimportant and uninteresting. Now I can see this as a mild precursor of what John's death has brought.

As I continue on my way to an isolated corner of the world, I smile ruefully as I chide myself, "Distance, eh? Couldn't have gotten much more distant than this, could I?"

Chapter 3

Looking, Listening and Walking

Once I am ensconced in my cabin, I spend hours sitting on my porch looking at the rugged coastline and listening to the waves. The changes in the light and the wind hold my attention, seemingly endlessly. I watch in sun, in storm, in rain and in fog.

Sometimes gannets, graceful white sea birds, whirl in, diving like pelicans. Usually that signals the arrival of pods of pilot whales. Three or six or twenty of them swim purposefully from one side of the cove to the other, their dorsal fins and smooth black bodies gracefully arcing in rhythm with each other. Or they frolic around, especially if a whale-watching tour boat stops in their midst. I can imagine, although I can't hear it, the high-pitched singing of the whales being picked up on a small underwater microphone, and the awed, delighted whispers of the passengers. After three or four or ten minutes the whales swim off and the captain restarts his motor and takes off.

Fishing boats come back, moving from left to right in my field of vision, starting around 9 a.m. Occasionally, if I'm not sleeping, I come out and see their lights, moving from right to left, as they go out to the fishing banks before dawn.

As I watch, I know there is activity below me. Campers are arriving and leaving. Sightseers of varying attitudes arrive, stop and ask the campground owners or passing campers all kinds of questions. "Is this Bear Cove?" "Isn't there any restaurant here?" "Why do you charge for the picnic tables?" "Does the road just end here?" "Is this all there is to Bear Cove?" "What's it famous for?"

John and I had been asked these questions just last summer when we'd found Ken and Sadie McLellan's small campground. It is billed as being "at the end of the road where the Saint Lawrence

Seaway meets the Atlantic Ocean." And that's where it is, perched on the bluff at the head of the cove. As soon as we saw it, we knew that we were right to have driven all the way out to a private campground with no trees, even though our usual preference was for a national, state or provincial park with lots of trees. And, as day after day went by, we kept postponing our departure, until, finally, we could do so no longer. Last year we had been amused by all the questions of the "day-trippers" and by the constant change in the campers.

Now, however, I cannot face those questions again. Fortunately, isolated on my secluded porch, I can see none of that activity.

Sometimes I walk. The short hike up to Little Grassy, the knoll above the campground, is a regular trip. Less often I climb Bear Cove Mountain. Steeper, longer, reputedly the haunt of bears, it is also more remote, less peopled. Once up there, I wander among the flowers and the views. The daisies are particularly profuse, and they too remind me of my father, who loved daisies more than any other flower. Sitting in the ridge between two higher elevations near the top of Bear Cove Mountain, I lose myself in vistas of the tree-covered, undulating river valley below me.

When I am haunted by memories made painful by my loss, when I feel they will surely overtake me, I can only escape their grasp through relentless activity. Then I take refuge in nature and

strike out for the lighthouse, down the coast along the headlands and back along the Lowland Cove Trail until I am completely exhausted and the feelings have departed for a while. There I meet the cows and horses who pasture on publicly owned land among spectacular views of cliff and coast. I go past the trail that leads seventeen miles south to Pollett Cove and then to Pleasant Bay, and remember my fantasies last year of sometime taking that hike. That fantasy seems even farther from reality this year than it did last.

One chilly, dreary night after I am caught in the rain on my way back from a walk to the lighthouse, I build a fire in the fireplace in the cabin. As I crumple old newspapers and arrange the kindling and firewood, I find myself mentally back in the early 1970s. I remember those days when feminism was born, and the voices of angry women were hurled publicly at men, berating them for their sins of dominance over, and exploitation of, women.

Those angry voices from the outside world spoke to something inside me. A young mother at the time, I loved my sons and loved doing things with them and taking care of them. Still, something was missing. I was living my childhood dreams. I had a husband who was a young, promising professor at a prestigious university, two adorable sons, a house of our own in a charming neighborhood, a stimulating and interesting social life—what more could I want? And yet I found myself dissatisfied, angry and depressed much of the time. Food became my source of comfort and solace, but then I hated myself for being too fat. It was easy to decide that John was the source of my unhappiness, especially in the atmosphere of those times. His shortcomings were symbolized for me by his failure to build fires in our newly acquired fireplace. I had fantasies of leaving him.

The only problem was it was hard to identify what John was doing wrong that might justify leaving him. It had to be something more than just not building fires! It seems funny now, but it was deadly serious back then.

I decided I had to be able to identify and name just how John was the source of my unhappiness. Maybe then I would leave him. What made me hesitate? My parents' example of sticking together in spite of deep differences, arguments and heated disagreements? The values of the time in which I was raised? An intellectual honesty imbedded deep in my nature? Fear of being alone? Hard to know.

So, in the middle of my discontent I went to the library to look for books that would tell me what John's failings as a husband were. I knew he was sometimes insensitive to my needs, was stubborn, and could be judgmental and unyielding. But he would usually listen, at least eventually, and I knew he loved me and our sons. I felt I had to be able to identify something more than these occasional difficult edges to his personality to justify leaving him.

To my initial dismay, what I found instead were books that said if you marry someone who is neurotic, you do it out of your own neurotic needs. In other words, even if I could identify something really wrong with John, it wouldn't let me off the hook. According to the books, it takes two to make an unhappy marriage. That slowed me down. Either I had to ignore everything I was reading, or it was time to turn my scrutiny toward myself. That wasn't easy and, at the time, I had no role models for doing so. But the message I was reading rang true, and I was miserable with things the way they were. So I didn't feel I had much choice unless I wanted to continue being miserable, and I started looking within myself for the source of my unhappiness.

Once I turned inward, I discovered I had plenty of work to do on myself. There was no longer any time or energy to try to find John's problems while mine were staring me in the face. And I needed help. Fortunately, I found it. Through a friend who was a counselor, I eventually located a psychiatrist who gently, sympathetically, but unrelentingly taught me how to identify the sources of unhappiness within myself. Over the years I saw him I learned to face a lot of things about myself that I did not want to face.

Learning to deal with my problems took my full attention and I no longer felt the need to fix John. This gave him the space to deal with his problems himself. Remarkable how that worked! He became much easier to live with once I gave up trying to change him.

Somewhere along the way, I decided that if I was dependent on John, that was my problem, not his. Symbolic of my increased willingness to take responsibility for my own life was my newfound determination to learn to build fires myself. Once I did, I enjoyed my ability to make one whenever I wanted it. We had them more often, and a festering source of resentment against John was completely removed.

Now, as the flames spread from the kindling to the logs, and the warmth and cheer radiate throughout the room, I sit back on my heels, grateful to have this skill. I move an easy chair closer to the hearth and continue my reflections as I watch the never-ending variety of the flames, and occasionally add more wood.

That was our first great crisis. I never thought our marriage would survive. Our tenth wedding anniversary was one of the unhappiest days of my life. In the middle of my misery, I had a most improbable vision of us, happily married and celebrating our twenty-fifth wedding anniversary surrounded by loving family and friends. How quixotic! How unlikely!

Yet at the time of John's death we'd been married almost thirty-three years. I used to say I had known the best of marriages and the worst of marriages, and I'd only been married once. Of course, at its worst, it was not nearly as bad as other marriages I have since heard and read about.

But it's hard to imagine any marriage better than ours had been the last ten years. That part of our marriage had been so happy, so satisfying, so fulfilling that I still can't imagine enjoying life again without the gusto, the laughter, the companionship and just the sheer joy we felt in each other's presence. Those qualities had become so much a part of our everyday existence, we sometimes took them for granted. Not often, however. Maybe it was an unanticipated benefit of the difficulties we went through that we hardly ever did take each other or our happy marriage for granted.

What had kept us together during those difficult years? I've often wondered which factors were most important. Both of us had been raised to believe marriage was forever. That made both of us unwilling to give up easily. Besides, even at the lowest point of our marriage, I knew John was a loving, caring father—as I was a loving, caring mother. Both of us felt keenly the responsibility we had undertaken by choosing to have children and both of us believed children deserve to be brought up by two good parents whenever possible.

I've also had to confess to myself I was more afraid of being on my own than I ever would have admitted then. It was part of what kept us together. Also, as time went on, I was aware of a grudging, but growing, recognition that John wanted what was best for me, and was willing to change in ways that would nurture our love, as was I.

The final factor is one some would call luck, but which I call God's hand at work in our lives. Almost in spite of ourselves, we had chosen well in deciding to marry each other. We were well suited. Our temperaments balanced each other's. Our interests and values were similar. When things began to look bleak, I got the help I needed to get back on track, and both of us were willing to make changes.

The feelings stirred up by my reverie in front of the fire last long after it dies down to embers and then, gradually, turns to gray ash. In bed that night my head and heart are still swirling with memories and emotions. What a shame we, in one sense, made so little of those early years of our marriage. Now, with our years of companionship cut short, I wish we had started the good parts earlier. More painfully, our sons spent a number of their childhood years with parents who didn't yet know how to be happily married. Without that we could not really, despite our love and our best intentions, be good parents. I wish I had been the mother they deserved to have in those early years. Still, in spite of all, I am grateful that we were able to turn our marriage and our lives around. And I have done everything I know to do to make amends to our sons, successfully, I hope.

I had vowed I would never again let them down the way I had then. Am I letting them down now by retreating into my own world? Am I so absorbed in my own grief and need for solitude that I am abandoning them in their grief? I fall asleep wondering.

Chapter 4

Family

The next morning is sunny, clear and cold. After breakfast I walk down to the campground and call Jim from the pay phone in back of the small office. His business doesn't officially open until 9:00 a.m., but he answers, as always, with a cheerful, "Cyclic Software."

"Jim, it's your Mom. It's good to hear your voice. How are you?"

"Mom." His voice lets me know that he's glad to hear mine. "I'm fine. Although the weather is beastly here. Hot and muggy. Not surprisingly."

One of the pleasures of these last few years has been Jim's geographical—and emotional—closeness to us. With him living less than two miles from our apartment in Washington, D.C., we have seen him often.

"You know, I really don't miss that at all," I reply. "It's nice and cool up here. So, what have you been up to?"

"Well, last weekend, WABA finally got the National Park Service to close the George Washington Parkway for a whole day. Natch, course, I had to bike it, even though it was hotter than I would have liked. Still, it was nice. It probably was nicer, too, for the people walking with no traffic noise along the trail we walked last Christmas."

I was familiar with the Washington Area Bicyclists Association, or WABA, as it was affectionately known. They met at our church and were the source of much of the helpful information Jim passed on to me to assist in my biking explorations. They were also instrumental in improving the biking opportunities in the area, a goal which I heartily supported. Jim, an avid bicyclist and someone who had no desire to ever own a car, followed their activities closely and often attended their meetings.

"So, how was the view, compared with the view we had on our walk?"

"Well, obviously not as close to the river. Or as rocky. But there are some nice high views of Georgetown which you do not see from the path. And, of course, you get a better view by bike than by car because it goes by more slowly."

"Sounds nice. Maybe they'll do it again sometime when I'm in town."

"Maybe. It seemed to go well with no huge outcries from the banned drivers."

"So, how's business?"

"Not bad. We have some new customers, and plans are moving along on our second new service line."

Jim knows better than to burden me with too many details of his software business. My limited knowledge of the intricacies of the cutting edge of computer technology is all too obvious. It is a tribute to his ability to explain what he does, and why he thinks it is important, that I understand anything about his business at all. And he does occasionally remind me that, compared with many, I am a computer whiz. But this newest service line has come up during the time of John's death and memorial service, and both of us know that my ability to focus on it has been too limited the last few months for it to be worth his while to go into any details at all. I am really proud of the fact that his business is a going concern some three years after he launched it on a shoestring, with a few other collaborators, a deep knowledge of the computer industry, his inherent intelligence and a lot of hope his only assets.

"Having Ron working full-time is a real help. He really understands the business pretty well by now."

"Glad to hear it's working out." I pause. It isn't easy for me to talk about my complex thoughts and feelings of the night before on the telephone. But, given the circumstances, it is either talk on the telephone or not talk about it at all. "I really called to say I am afraid I am so absorbed in my own grief that I am neglecting you. How are you doing?"

"Well, I don't feel neglected, although I do miss our walks and our dinners." I smile. Although he is a pretty good cook when he wants to be, Jim really doesn't like cooking for himself. He hesitates before going on. "I don't really know how I'm doing about dealing with Dad's death. It seems kind of unreal. Sort of like he's back teaching in Ann Arbor, and will be here some weekend soon." For the last six years, until he retired, John had commuted back to Ann Arbor during the semesters he was teaching, and returned to Washington those weekends when I didn't travel to visit him in his small furnished, efficiency apartment in Ann Arbor.

Jim's next pause is longer, but I know he sometimes needs time to put his feelings into words accurately. "As it happens, I met someone on the WABA ride whose mother recently died. Talking to him has been a big help. And Heather and Beth invited me over to dinner. They were both very sympathetic."

I am relieved he has found someone he can talk to who has experienced a similar loss, and that Heather and Beth, two of his college friends, have reached out to him. Still, my heart aches. He is so young to lose a parent. And I know from my own experience how much my relationships with my parents evolved after I had supposedly reached the age of adulthood. I am really sad that his relationship with his father, while it had certainly changed and improved over time, would forever remain as it was when he was a young adult.

"Well, you know how to reach me if you want me, don't you?"

"Yes, I still have the number you gave me for the campground."

"Please call me if you want me to come back home or if you just want to talk. You know how much I love you, and miss you."

"Yes, Mom, I do. And I love you, too."

I hang up the phone with a lump in my throat. Much as I love him and miss him, I still can hardly imagine going back home and making any pretense of picking up the strands of my life. Besides, I don't think it would be good for either of us if I were to lean on Jim too much in this time of loss, and I know what a temptation it would be to do that if I were back in D.C.

No, it is much better for me to be up here until I am ready to pick up my own life back in D.C. I think of Mom and how wise she was to wait until she had established a life of her own, apart from the life she and Dad had shared, after his death before she moved to Eau Claire to be closer to my sister Sonia. It was both smart and lucky that she found an apartment of her own near Sonia, developed her own friends and found her own church home. Just when her health made it difficult for her to live on her own, they found the perfect house in the same neighborhood with a separate apartment for Mom. She cherished the closeness to Sonia and her family at the same time she cherished the ability to maintain a separate life.

Since it is only 6 a.m. on the west coast where Tor is, I climb up Bear Cove Mountain and think about the difference between loneliness and missing someone. Fifteen, twenty, a hundred times a day I miss John. And yet, in a way at least, although I am heavy-hearted almost beyond words, I'm not really lonely. I was loneliest, in the midst of family, on my tenth wedding anniversary when I was convinced that John was the source of my unhappiness.

At 8 a.m., Tor's time, I call him.

"Oh, hi Mom."

"Busy?" I can tell by the tone of his voice he is in a hurry.

"I have a client coming in this morning for a recording session, but I have a few minutes."

I explain again my fear that I am neglecting him in my own grief.

"Oh, Mom, that's nice of you to think of, but I'm doing OK." Long pause. "Not that it's easy to deal with." I hate the fact that he has to deal with it. Especially since John's death occurred just as Tor had pretty much recovered from his ex-wife's departure and their ensuing divorce after only nineteen months of marriage. "It has kind of hit me with a double whammy. I hadn't really thought much about the divorce lately, but now I feel again some of the awful feelings I suffered then. Not, of course, in the same way. Luckily, there was nothing negative in my relationship with Dad. And I have lots of good memories."

"It seems so unfair."

"Yeah, well, I got through the divorce; I'll get through this, too. Stephanie's invited me to go camping with them again, soon, and I think I will. Being with them is a great antidote to grief." I reflect briefly on our last visit, and on the cheerful hubbub that is the usual state of affairs in my daughter's happy, busy household.

"Do you want me to come out to visit?"

"I'd love to see you, but I'm not sure it would help. I think this is something I have to work out for myself. Anyway, I'd kind of like to plan a visit to D.C. after you get back." Whenever that is, I think. "Besides," he continues, "I understand what you're doing and think it's important. Remember how I needed to learn to like being alone after my divorce?"

"You're great, Tor. But let me know if you change your mind . . . or if you'd like to come up here. It's lovely. And lots of good hiking."

"I will. Oops, have to go. I can keep this client waiting a few minutes, but I've used those up."

"I love you, Tor."

"I love you, too, Mom."

After we hang up, I sit on the dilapidated leather banquette by the phone for a few minutes, feeling cheered by the conversations, the sun, the walking and the calico cat who joined me as I talked and now lies purring in my lap. For good measure I call Stephanie, but she isn't home.

Chapter 5

Greta's Visit

During Mother's final years my sister Greta, the youngest in our family, perfected her gift of knowing just what Mom needed to feel special and loved in times of crisis, and to see that it arrived at the perfect time and in the perfect way. Medical discussions were a trial for her, and hospitals were difficult for her to enter. It was easier for her to stock Mom's freezer for when she came home, and she did that with love, imagination and thoughtfulness. Greta's special dishes, healthful and appetizing, helped Mom hold her own against her aging and failing body's tendency to lose weight. On visits to her various hospital rooms, during Mother's frequent stays, Greta brought and arranged exotic flowers and tended them each day. When Mom was ready to come home, Greta came bearing gifts of gourmet meals and practical yet feminine cotton nightgowns.

Mom started her career as a real estate broker at the age of fifty-nine, after a lifetime of being a wife and mother. Greta and I beat her, but not by too much. I graduated from law school the year I turned forty-four and Greta graduated from engineering school at the age of forty. Firmly rooted, with her husband Rich and their three beloved Scotties, in St. Paul, Minnesota, she was limited in job choices by a wan economy, her age and her gender. Contract jobs provided a way for her to learn her craft in different settings while continuing to look for the right permanent job. Providentially, Greta had several intervals between jobs at times important to her and the family. After Mom's death, she had the time, the impulse and the energy to go through her smaller things and select valued mementos for Mom's special friends and relatives. In the process she came to learn more about herself as well as to appreciate Mom in new ways.

Anticipating another transition, Greta promised me at John's memorial service that she would come and visit. How like her to know the perfect timing. After several weeks of solitude, I am delighted to get a letter proposing a visit. For the first time since I arrived up here, I am ready for some understanding, nurturing and undemanding companionship, and can think of no one better able to provide that than Greta.

Even so, I am surprised at how glad I am to see her when she comes down the jetway with her jaunty step, hair in one long braid hanging down her back and a shopping bag looking like it is full of goodies.

"Greta, it is so good to see you!" She sets down her shopping bag and gives me a big hug, and I feel tears stinging my eyes for the first time in weeks.

"It's my pleasure," she responds, leaning back to really scrutinize me. "You look like the northern air is agreeing with you."

"Well, I guess I do look and feel better than I did at the memorial service. At least I have been sleeping." Since the two of us are the primary inheritors of the insomnia both our mother and grandmother suffered with all their lives, she understands immediately.

"Well, that's a good sign. The chance to come up here, to a new part of the world for me, is all the more reason to be glad I have a few weeks free." Greta definitely has inherited our father's love of exploring new places.

"I just needed to get away." I know Greta understands. She has always had a need to have her own space and wisely has made life decisions that make this possible. She and her husband, who is also an engineer, have a close and loving relationship in which each respects the other's separate identity, friends and interests. The two of them rejoice in being themselves, separately and together. Despite Rich's interests in space and space travel, he doesn't really like flying on planes much, and is not the avid voyager she is. So I know, for Greta, the chance to come visit me in a place new to her is an added bonus.

It's warm when we leave the airport. I look at Greta, "I hope your swimming suit is easy to reach. There's a great place to go swimming on our way back."

"Would I come to a place surrounded by water without an easily accessible swimming suit? You know me better than that!" And she pulls a brightly colored suit out of the bag she had with her on the airplane. Growing up on a lake, both of us learned to swim early and love it, especially when we are unfettered by crowds, ropes and officious lifeguards.

Just before we get to Port Hood, we stop in the small, unheralded county park on the Gulf of St. Lawrence that John and I found last summer. We change into our swimming suits behind the big towel we hold for each other, giggling like school kids. I realize with a start that I can't remember the last time I laughed. After our swim in the warm, clear waters of the Gulf, we dry off and, towels wrapped around us, walk on the boardwalk.

"Oh, Greta, I thought of you last year when we saw so many unfamiliar birds along here. John was useless at identifying birds. They were all 'lesser pipsqueaks' to him!" Over the last few years Greta has become an avid birdwatcher. Her interest has piqued my curiosity. Unfortunately, due to my less-than-perfect vision and my sporadic attention to birds, my ability to identify various species has remained minimal. Somehow, it makes me happy that she is able to identify the birds we see, even though I know I am likely to remember only a fraction of what she tells me.

Our next stop is to shop for groceries at the supermarket in Chéticamp, some thirty miles south of the cabin. Her enthusiasm and wealth of ideas make me realize how limited my diet has become: cereal, bananas, peanut butter and jam, uninspired hamburger and macaroni hot dishes and ice cream. Even with the limited selection of a small-town store, she pokes and sniffs, combines foods in her mind, plans menus and stimulates my dormant taste buds. She has, of course, brought a few of her gourmet specialties with her.

While Greta is poking around, my mind flashes back to the time after Dad died. I remember thinking if I were in Mom's shoes, I would just close myself up in my house and eat. I smile as I reflect on the difficulties of predicting how we are going to react to anything in life. Back then, the idea of grieving by restlessly stalking foreign hills would never have occurred to me.

The Rusty Anchor in Pleasant Bay is our dinner destination. I had known she would appreciate the distinctive Cape Breton fish cakes, and she does. Over dinner I tell her about our visit here last summer, in a storm, and how I ate as much of John's fish cakes as I could get away with, since I hadn't ordered them. In the parking lot I suddenly find myself in tears for the first time since I left Washington. Greta hugs me and I cling to her and cry for my loss.

Even though it is after 10 p.m. when we get to the cabin, the western sky is still light enough for Greta to appreciate the magnificent location. We sit on the porch talking and watching the stars come out and the moon rise.

Chapter 6

Pictures from the Past

Greta pampers me lavishly during her stay, and I gratefully accept every special food and thoughtful touch she offers. After we left home, Mother always made a point of pampering us when we came back to visit. I feel now as though Greta's ministrations are a reflection of both her and Mother's love, and I guess they are.

One rainy morning we feast on a sumptuous breakfast of sourdough whole wheat pancakes, topped, for our first helping, with sweet potato butter and sour cream and then, for our second course, with whipped pecan butter and real maple syrup. In honor of the occasion I make a fire, move the table in front of it and prepare a pot of Darjeeling tea. We both revel in the elegance and sensuous pleasures of the warm fire contrasting with the rain sounding on the roof, the varied and delectable tastes and textures of the breakfast and the pleasure of each other's company. For a brief time the ache in my heart subsides, although I'm still aware of it.

After we have wrung every last drop of pleasure out of the meal, I clear away the dishes and even enjoy washing them in the hot, soapy water. When I come back to the fire, Greta has begun sorting out pictures she brought with her. As I join her, we laugh and reminisce, picking up old, familiar pictures from our childhood years.

"Greta, this was such a good idea. I guess if there was life and laughter before John entered my life, I should be able to experience it after he is gone."

"I know what an important part of your life he was. I can't even imagine how I'll get by if I ever lose Rich, and we've only been married fifteen years." Almost every woman I know assumes that she will be a widow some day and tries to prepare for it. I had, too, without even being conscious of it. Greta goes on, "But I did think these pictures might help."

While we are talking, I open a manila envelope and idly begin sorting through the pictures. Suddenly I freeze. In my hand I am holding a picture of me with the neighborhood children when I was seven. Unbidden, memories from that long-ago summer assail me. Unwillingly, I am transported back in time.

It's a nice summer afternoon. Mom and Dad are in the back yard, washing the porch windows. I have been helping and enjoying the harmonious mood of a family working together. The two neighbor boys, who are nine and thirteen, come over and ask me to go down to the lake by the farm to play. I hang back, knowing what they mean, but Mom and Dad urge me to go along and play, thinking that is what I really want to do. They don't sense my uncertainty, confusion and dread, and I don't know how to express it.

We stop next door to pick up Susie, two years younger than I. Then the boys lead us down to the old boathouse, now high and dry on the shore and surrounded by quick-growing willow trees. We are completely isolated here from the houses up the hill. The boys expose themselves, urinate from a tree to impress us, take us into the boathouse and force us to perform oral sex. I am horrified, flattered by their attention, titillated and scared all at once. They warn me not to say anything, and I know that I couldn't even without the warning. I don't have the vocabulary and I am too confused.

Abruptly the scene changes. I am on our front porch, lying on the daybed, crying. Mother has just talked to me. Somehow, she found out about what happened and spoke in tones that convinced me I had done something terribly wrong. I am mortified, humiliated, ashamed and very much alone.

Something about my body language and the look on my face alerts Greta to the dramatic change in my mood.

"Kirsten, what's wrong?" she asks with concern.

"Oh, Greta, look." I hold out my hand with the picture. Greta looks at it, and then back at me with puzzled solicitude. "Remember that terrible Easter weekend seven years ago?"

"Of course. How could I forget?"

"That's the last time I saw this picture. I was remembering what occurred the summer it was taken."

"Ahh," Greta responds as comprehension dawns.

We both remember, vividly, the visit I made to Mom's apartment in Eau Claire, Wisconsin, shortly after she moved there to be near my sister Sonia and her family. I had come to try to understand and heal the most hidden part of my childhood. It had started as a joint effort between me and Mother on a long Easter weekend to explore our memories and pictures from the period. It ended with us at a crossroad where neither of us was sure whether the relationship would be rejuvenated and thrive, would wither, or be torn asunder.

"You were so wonderful. I remember how you came and got me on Saturday when I was so confused and in such pain that I knew I couldn't spend another night under Mother's roof. I couldn't believe it when I found out that she never told anyone about it, not even Dad. And she never made any connection between my unhappiness in second grade that fall and what happened in the summer. But the worst was when she became defensive, protective toward the neighbors, and minimized what had happened and its impact on me."

"I wonder why she did that," Greta muses.

"Well, I always wondered if something similar had happened to her when she was a girl. Her reaction felt so much like that of someone who has been abused herself and who reacts out of those childish feelings, rather than as an adult."

"Did you ever ask her about that?" Greta inquires.

"Yes, I did, but she couldn't remember anything." I pause for a moment, remembering. "When I called you to come get me, I knew Mother needed help dealing with her part of what happened, and I knew I needed help. It was painfully obvious we couldn't help each other at that point. You were great. Remember? The bus broke down and you drove all the way from St. Paul to get me. I was so relieved to get to the safety and comfort of your car and then your home."

"I was so glad I could be there for you. You had always been there for me. It made me feel so sad to think of you as a vulnerable, unprotected and emotionally abandoned seven-year-old child." It was true that I, twelve years older than Greta, and ten years older than Sonia, had loved taking care of my little sisters. For me, it was a cross between playing with dolls and practicing the art of mothering. It was also true that twice in my teenage years I had taken over for Mother, once when she was in the hospital for surgery, and once when she went to a church conference.

"You were sort of a back-up mother," Greta continues. "Mom had her own problems those years and couldn't always be there for us."

We are both silent. I think of Mom and her childhood, marred by illness and the death of a younger brother. "You know, she always said she didn't have a childhood herself," I remember. "That would make it hard to guide your children through childhood."

Greta nods in agreement. "That's why it was so nice to have you. Remember how you read to us when you came home from college? You introduced us to Winnie the Pooh and the A.A. Milne poems and all kinds of children's literature."

"Yes, I do, and it wasn't just children's literature. I bet you were the only six-year-old who listened to *Tale of Two Cities* from beginning to end!" I remember both Sonia and Greta enjoying those summer evenings together as I read through the book, chapter by chapter, after I had been introduced to it in my freshman year of college. Greta, especially, had a reverence and a tactile appreciation for that book, and others, as she was growing up. And both of them had completely understood and appreciated the complex tale of intrigue and drama from long, long ago.

"And now I get to benefit from your love of books whenever you pass a good one on to me. You're the only person who sends me good new fiction and biography," I say, glancing appreciatively at the four new volumes sitting on the coffee table. We share smiles, enjoying the bonds of mutual appreciation and shared interests we have forged over the years.

Reluctantly, I bring the subject back to our earlier discussion. "You know, I brought along my own envelope from that Easter. I might as well get it so I can look at it with the benefit of your experience and support. I must have kept that envelope and stuck it in with my stuff for this trip for a reason."

In a minute I return from my bedroom with the envelope. We look through the scraps of paper from my ubiquitous yellow legal pads, filled with my agonized attempts to make sense of what Mom was telling me that weekend. My astonishment at her failure to tell Dad, or anyone else, came through the pages as clearly as though I were sitting in her living room today. I remember those feelings. But I'd forgotten her letters to me. Greta and I take turns reading them, putting them in order when we can.

"Look at this," Greta exclaims indignantly. "Here she is, in July, saying that nothing ever happened! How could she?"

"I'd forgotten that," I say, taking the letter from her and reading it. "I think it was about that time when I told her I couldn't talk to her on the phone any more. She was in such deep denial, I couldn't deal with the subject with her any more. After all, she was the person who brought it up shortly before my visit, and I have all too many memories of it. Not until she mentioned it again had I begun to realize its impact. I had thought of it as 'just harmless sex play.' But, as my therapist helped me realize, that's not what's happening when one of the boys is a teenager and the girl is only seven."

We're both quiet, reading through the letters. Finally, we sit back and look at each other. I speak first, "You know, these are really a remarkable set of letters."

"Yes, they are," Greta agrees. "You can see her going all the way from the depths of denial in July to repentance, despair and acceptance. I especially like this," she says, reaching for one of the later letters. "Listen to this: 'If I think only of the many misjudgments I've made, I cannot survive. I have to believe the wonderful news that we hold as Christians, that we can be forgiven any sin.' "

"And she really did believe that," I reply. "She was an amazing woman. Little did I know when I brought the subject up again that Easter, for my own sake, how much it would mean to her in the end."

"The irony is that, once she stopped needing outside affirmation, because she was finally at peace with herself," Greta notes, "people loved to be in her company and showered her with affirmation."

"It wasn't hard to do. She really faced what she'd hidden from everyone, including herself, for all those decades. She felt the magnitude of her failure in the one area of her life which was more important to her than anything else—her children—and the hurt caused by that failure. Once she'd done so and accepted her responsibility for it, she was able to accept God's forgiveness. Only then was she able to forgive herself and be rid of the heavy burden of an unknown, unnamed guilt."

"Not an easy thing for anyone to do, especially in the space of less than a year, with no professional help."

"But wasn't she lucky to have Meg?" I respond.

If there are angels placed on earth in certain times and places to help people, Meg was surely one of them. For a few critical years, just when she needed her, Meg was Mother's minister. These two devoutly religious, smart, inquiring, articulate, courageous women had formed a bond from their first meeting. They exchanged books, ideas and tea. They laughed together, exulted over signs of spiritual progress wherever they saw them and commiserated over signs of sinfulness and pain in the world.

Meg literally was the agent of Mom's salvation during that dark summer and fall. They talked, they prayed, Meg comforted Mother and let her cry on her shoulder. And, once, Meg even snapped at Mother in exasperation. Mom's painful journey toward self-knowledge and acceptance was aided by Meg and by my sister Sonia, who managed to lovingly and prayerfully support both Mother and me during this period.

"You know," I continue, "it was only after we confronted the hard truths about our relationship that I could fully appreciate the ways in which she was a good mother to me. I remember watching her care for Peter and talk baby talk to him. Remember he was born shortly after we were reconciled." We both smile as we think of sturdy, cheerful Peter, Sonia's youngest. "She must have cared for me just as tenderly when I was a baby. And she was great when I called home from Oberlin to tell her I was pregnant. You know how strict her Norwegian Lutheran upbringing was. Still, she never reproached me. She just told me she loved me, I should come home, we would work things out and that the most important thing was not to let myself become bitter."

"That sounds like Mom at her best." Greta pauses and tilts her head the way she does sometimes when she is struck by a new thought. "What really stands out in these letters Mom wrote to you is her persistence. She could have given up, or have blamed you for the estrangement. But she didn't. She didn't let her pain or confusion or uncertainty or fear stop her."

"Yup. She never gave up where her children were concerned."

"You know," Greta says thoughtfully, "in a way you're looking for the same kind of redemption she experienced. You could have just succumbed to numbness, and lived your life out as a lonely, grieving widow. Instead, you've come up here to heal so you can go on with a meaningful life."

I lean back and, frowning in concentration, stare into the fire as I think about what Greta has just said. I muse aloud, "That's an interesting parallel. There does seem to be something in me—and in you—that isn't willing to just make do with our circumstances. And that's the same quality that gave Mom the strength to persevere and ultimately triumph over her own history." My brow clears, and I turn to Greta with a smile. "Thank you, little sister. That's a really inspiring insight."

Greta responds with a broad grin. "Thanks. I think maybe you've been underestimating yourself!"

"Who, me?" I exclaim in mock horror. "Couldn't be!"

Laughing, we both rise, stretch and go out to the porch. It has turned into a beautiful day, and we race each other to Little Grassy. As we reach the top, winded, and flop down on the grass, Greta recovers her breath first. "I still miss Mom."

"Me, too. I wish she were here now. I sure could use her wisdom about how to survive gracefully as a widow. I think that her best years—at least emotionally and spiritually—may have been after she was a widow."

Mom's death a little over three years ago was both a terrible loss and a wonderful relief. Suffering from a chronic, untreatable lung infection as a result of her untreated severe childhood respiratory illnesses, she feared most she would die struggling for breath. It was a blessing that, instead, her heart began to fail. Ironically, during the same time her emotional and spiritual health were improving, her body was gradually giving out. Again and again, she would have a medical crisis: pneumonia; severe, seemingly intractable bladder infections; congestive heart failure; strokes. Again and again, she would struggle back, go through the stages of grief about having lost a little more of her strength, her mobility, her energy and her independence each time. Again and again, she would come to acceptance of her new, more limited status, and an appreciation of all she did have.

"I remember the last time I talked to her," I continue, "a few days before her final stroke. I called her at home, from work, just on a whim. She described how happy she was, sitting in her sunny living room. I could picture it as she talked, with all of the homey touches that made it such a warm, welcoming place. She said she'd been rereading the book by M. Scott Peck I'd given her for Christmas. She told me how lucky she felt to be able to live by herself and yet be close to Sonia and Eric and their kids."

When her final stroke left her without the ability to walk or swallow, she was very clear, despite the severe aphasia that made it difficult for her to formulate a sentence. But she could understand everything. And she could let us know what she wanted. She did not want to be kept alive by artificial means. She was ready to die.

For the final three days of her life, her hospital room was a happy place. Greta brought flowers. Sonia's friends brought flowers. Friends visited. Cards arrived. She talked on the telephone to my brother, Rolf, John, Jim, Tor and Stephanie. Tor and Rolf headed to her bedside, Rolf by car with his wife and four children, and Tor by plane. She was alert when Tor arrived at 1:30 a.m. on Palm Sunday, her 65th wedding anniversary. She was alert when Rolf arrived at 3:30 a.m. She gave both of them big smiles. She told Rolf it was fine if he went to get some sleep and came back in the morning with his whole family.

She died the next day, peacefully, with all of us gathered around, while a church service played on the TV. She died leaving no unfinished business, ready and eager to move on to the next stage of her existence. Those of us who believe in heaven have no doubt that is where she is.

Sonia's older daughter, Sofia, my mother's first granddaughter, buried her face in my stomach as she turned away from the bedside. I murmured into her hair, with tears streaming down my face as well, "You were very special to Grandma. We all were." And I realized then just how true that was. Whatever mistakes she had made in raising us, she had raised us all to know that we were each unique and valuable to her.

As the days go by, Greta and I talk about all of this. And about what a pleasure Mom was to be with in her last years. Greta, too, benefited from Mom's change after confronting her failure to protect me in my childhood. Greta's relationship with Mother had also changed, for the better. Mom was better able to appreciate Greta's gifts without placing unreasonable expectations on her.

Now, in talking over our shared memories of Mom and our deep love and appreciation for her, we two sisters are closer. Something has deepened in our relationship. Once again, Greta has provided a healing presence to me when I needed it. By caring for my physical and emotional needs, crying with me, listening to me and reminding me of Mom's resilience—and my own—she has lightened the burden of grief I am still carrying. Because of her visit, I am a little more able to imagine living fully again.

We both know that, wherever Mom is, she is aware of us now, and that she is grieving with me in my loss, rejoicing at our closeness and praying for all of us who were exceptional to her. Thinking of her, drawing strength from her memory, I finger her wedding ring, worn on a chain around my neck, and silently send thanks to her for being the mother she was.

Chapter 7

Stephanie

One clear, sunny day while Greta is visiting, she asks whether she can borrow my car and drive down the eastern coast of the Island. I appreciate her need for physical and emotional space after our closeness of the past few days and readily agree. In fact, I too feel the need to be alone with my thoughts for a while. After weeks of almost complete solitude, I welcome the companionship of my sister, but I also miss my times of idle reflections.

Once she is gone, however, I find myself restless. The day is warm and I don't feel like walking. Nor do I feel like just sitting on the porch. I wander around aimlessly until my eyes fall on the old, small attaché cases I brought from home. I'm not sure now, and wasn't sure when I put them in with my things to bring up here, why I bothered to bring them along. One has in it all the family letters from my desk. The other has all the letters I had saved from high school and college. I had taken them when Mother moved out of the house we grew up in. But my talks with Greta have stirred thoughts of my childhood, and I carry the cases out to the dining room table.

What a hodge-podge of letters! Some are from my sisters. They were faithful correspondents from a young age, when we were often separated because of the large age differences. I read their notes and letters, remembering how much I loved them from birth, and how much a part they were of the happy memories of my childhood. The correspondence is touching and funny and the memories of my sisters are nothing but sweet.

More painful are the memories stirred up by the letters I wrote but never mailed to boyfriends. How glad I am that I am past that teenaged anguish! From my sophomore year at Oberlin there are a whole series of letters written to a boyfriend I'd dated the summer before. Once I went back to college he kept up only a fragmentary relationship—much less in frequency or intensity than I had apparently expected. Unmailed letter after letter pours out my hurt, my anger, my bafflement.

I go to the kitchen to get myself a glass of iced tea and take it out on the porch. Sitting there, sipping my tea, I reflect on what I have been reading. I think of Tom, my long-lost boyfriend. He was a year or so older than I was. Working at one of the mills, he had never been to college or been a particularly good student. He was kind of drifting through life. It surprises me now that I invested so many dreams and hopes in this young man. In retrospect our lives were on different trajectories. It does not seem strange that he saw no future for us and, while not knowing how to end it, had no interest in investing a lot in a long-distance relationship that was destined to be short-term.

Why was Tom the kind of man I was dating? My mind flashes back to my 25th high-school reunion. I remember my encounter with Dave. Handsome and smart, he was the object of what I thought was an impossible crush in eighth grade. He went on to become an engineer and was then living in the Chicago area. Talking to him at the reunion, I was both amazed and amused to find out that he remembered dating me. I do not ever remember our dating. He intimated that *I* was the one who was not interested in pursuing the relationship! Was I, as the old country song goes, "looking for love in all the wrong places"? And, if so, why?

The image of my father's hurt after our trip with Jim and Tor to the train museum floats before my eyes. I had seen then the reason he experienced rejection from me was that he himself felt unworthy. Is that why I experienced such painful rejection from Tom? Is that why I couldn't believe someone smart and handsome could possibly be interested in me?

I was one of those children who are unnaturally good. I always followed the rules strictly. I was a good student and often regarded by my peers as a "teacher's pet." I was horrified when I found out in college that some of my high-school classmates had cut roses from other people's yards. I told Mother when I was in eighth grade the one thing she never had to worry about was that

I would lose my virginity before I was married. I had internalized the rule that good girls did not have sex outside of marriage, and I took it very seriously.

So why did I become pregnant just before my senior year at Oberlin? Why did I choose that way to rebel? In spite of my subsequent years of therapy, I can't really answer this question.

I do know that I had become involved in yet another relationship in college with someone who was not suitable. He was a good man, as were all my boyfriends, but he was thirteen years older than I, uneducated and a garage mechanic. My parents were deeply concerned when they found out, especially when I talked about marrying him. They brought in a doctor they knew to help counsel me. I was furious and appalled at their insensitivity. But they extracted a promise from me to change my plans and leave Oberlin, where he lived, for the summer. In hindsight I can, as a parent, appreciate their concern, although the way they went about trying to intervene was neither wise nor effective.

I spent that summer working as a waitress at a resort hotel on a small island off the coast of New England. It was a lovely place, and the hotel where I was employed had a beautiful, unspoiled beach. We waitresses had time each afternoon to read, talk, sunbathe and swim. One of the owners had a speedboat with water skiing equipment. He wanted to show that his was a lively resort that offered water sports in the glorious, balmy summer afternoons. Since nearly all the clientele had been coming to the place for decades, and were hardly youthful enough to want to be dragged over the water behind a speedboat, we got to use the skiing equipment to our hearts' content.

Sometimes the owners would bring a band in to play for dances. Afterwards one of them would drive the band back to the mainland after the ferry boats had stopped running for the night. I sometimes rode along. It was beautiful on the water at night. I loved the salt air. In the wake of the boat, I would watch the phosphorescence lighting up the dark water. I was entranced. Although someone explained that they were microscopic organisms that lit up when disturbed at night, I thought they were magical.

On my days off I would often take the ferry over to the mainland. Not that there was much to see there. But I liked the ferry.

Particularly on days when it was overcast and misty. The sea gulls, the sea smells and the boat all reminded me of Norway, which we had visited at the end of my senior year in high school.

It could have been a wonderful summer. But it wasn't, not really, although I do have some fond memories. I was acting out my anger at my parents. I drank too much. I smoked too much. I partied too much, and I experimented with sex. I worried my parents by hardly ever writing or calling. I took risks—once running away from a predatory man with whom I had flirted until it became clear that his intentions were anything but honorable. I went out the back door of the bar while he waited for me to come back from the rest room. I had walked miles home the back way that night, sobered by my close call, and looking over my shoulder to make sure I was not being followed. I escaped him, but made other unwise choices. And I became pregnant.

I wish now that I could have had the therapy I had later to help me figure out what was going on, instead of acting out my anger. Except that the result was Stephanie. Once again, God proved He can bring good even out of human rebellion and weakness. Perhaps my life story is one of the reasons I so love the many Old Testament stories of the wonderful ways in which God brings good about through flawed human beings. I'm no King David, but his story has some parallels to mine. It is a story of misplaced lust that led him to sin by murdering Uriah and marrying his widow, Bathsheba. When confronted with his sin, he repented. Out of this relationship, which began in sin, Solomon was born: Solomon, who became king, and under whom Israel flourished and prospered.

So, too, although I did not marry the father of my baby, I have repented of those actions that resulted in my bringing a baby into the world for whom I could not properly care. But, as I have come to know her, my only daughter, I have come to see that God works through her for good in many, many ways. Of course, at the time, I knew none of that. I only knew I was pregnant and unmarried in a time when that made me a social pariah.

By the time I went home from Oberlin, two months pregnant, I had already decided to put the baby up for adoption. Although my father talked of sending me to Sweden or Japan for an abortion, then illegal in the United States, that wasn't an option I took seriously. Apart from the mind-boggling question of where a poor millworker's family would get the money for it, I knew I could not abort the baby growing within me. My only conscious reason was I knew I wanted more children, and I couldn't have accepted it if I became sterile as a result of an abortion. There may have been other reasons. Now that I know how the story has worked itself out, I see God's hand.

Nor was keeping the baby an option I could accept. It is hard to remember now what a shameful thing it was thirty-six years ago to have and raise a child born "out of wedlock." I am not sure the phrase even exists in the American lexicon of today. The only people I knew who did it were people regarded by the world I lived in as women of loose moral character. In spite of my behavior that fateful summer, I did not put myself in that category, and I did not want my child raised with the stigma of having someone like that as a mother.

Mom and Dad had friends in Sacramento, a former minister and retired social worker and his wife, who opened their home to me. They were warm and accepting, and I devoted the five months I was with them to doing everything I could to give my baby a good start in life. I ate well, went to my doctor, slept well, walked and explored Sacramento. They had a marvelous library, and I remember spending hours curled up on the chaise longue in it, reading my way around the world. It was, strangely enough, a very peaceful time—at least, on the surface.

In those days California had a wonderfully open and welcoming policy toward mothers putting their babies up for adoption. They provided weekly counseling and paid for good medical care. This was the first counseling I ever had, and I needed it more than I knew. I went into it with trepidation. The method I had devised to get me through this period was characteristically Norwegian. I was determined to deal with this inconvenient fact of my pregnancy stoically and intellectually. My vision of my pregnancy was of a tube, in me, but not of me.

The first chink in my armor was revealed when my first social worker told me that she was being moved to another division. She tried to explore my feelings about the change, but I assured her I understood, it was not a problem, and I'd look forward to meeting the new counselor assigned to my case. This was all very convincing until I stood up to leave and fainted at her feet. With her help, and that of her successor, I gradually became aware of the welter of feelings beneath the surface. It was not surprising, as I delved deeper, that I was hanging on to that counselor as though she were my only lifeline, and her departure would doom me to isolation.

First, I acknowledged my deep shame. Despite my efforts to hide from my feelings, I couldn't escape my failure to live up to my own moral code—which was shared by my parents, my church and our society as a whole. My exile to California, although I freely chose it, also felt like an abandonment by my parents. And how could I blame them? I learned the first lesson of therapy: you can't resolve issues unless you admit them and talk about them. Only by forming a connection with a caring human being could I face my shame, and gradually begin to let go of it.

Then there were my fears. First of all, of the delivery itself. My sex education had consisted of one embarrassing talk with my mother (which was probably more than she had received from her prim and old-fashioned mother), and frequent reading of *Forever Amber*, a racy novel set in seventeenth-century England. The opening scene was of Amber's mother in gory childbirth which was, literally, the death of her. The fact that she was pregnant without benefit of marriage didn't do anything to assuage my fears. Neither did the overheard stories of the horrors of labor, including stories told by my mother. Although I read books on natural childbirth, I was still scared of the birth process itself.

Maybe my biggest fear was that if I let myself be aware of my feelings, I wouldn't be able to give my baby up for adoption. Intellectually I had figured out that it would be best for both of us if I did not keep her. Yet I had heard stories about women who were not able to give up their babies once they had seen them. I didn't want to do that. But I knew how much I loved my sisters when they were babies.

So, while calm on the surface, underneath I was a bubbling cauldron of emotions. It wasn't surprising that I didn't want to allow any of them to surface. Thanks to my social workers, however, I was able to take the lid off my feelings and share them. I became less afraid, and learned that I was actually better able to handle them when I verbalized my anguish in the presence of someone who was skilled at dealing with emotions and who was not herself frightened by them.

Thanks to California's generosity and these caring women, I was able to accept the experience, instead of pretending that it was happening to someone else. The birth was lonely, more painful than it would have been had I known more then and happened with me anesthetized just before the actual delivery. Afterwards I talked to Mom without being able to express the confusing welter of feelings I was experiencing, and, briefly, to my daughter's birth father.

I took the train home five days after Stephanie was born. Before I went I signed the adoption papers. That was the only time I saw her until she was twenty-seven years old, married and the mother of a young son, Chris. In the intervening years I thought of her often. I second-guessed my decision to give her up for adoption frequently. I imagined meeting her somewhere. I prayed for her and wondered about her life. Even as I married John and raised our two sons, her absence was a part of my life.

We were able to contact each other through the county adoption agency I had used. I had told them I wanted to know if she ever wanted to look for me. Fortunately, I had told John about her birth when we started to become seriously interested in each other. No one else knew outside my family of origin, and a few close friends in college.

The day the letter came, eight years ago, John and I were in the middle of a festering argument about, of all things, Mother's Day. When I came home that day and saw a letter from the Department of Social Services of the County of Sacramento, California, I guessed it held news of my daughter. Why else would I be getting mail from the Sacramento Department of Social Services? I held up the letter, looked heavenward, and asked God if He was sure this was the right time. As usual, God was right.

Stephanie and I exchanged letters. To write a letter to your daughter whom you do not know is a difficult, exciting, scary, indescribable experience. I do not remember what I wrote. I still have her letter. Periodically, I reread it. It always makes me feel wonderful. She wrote of her wonder at being able to write to me. She wrote of how she knew it was the right time to complete the circle for both of us because things had fallen into place so easily. Little did she know, as she wrote, that my experience, too, has been that when my plans are in accord with God's will, they fall into place easily. When they are not, it doesn't happen.

She wrote of the place I, her unknown birth mother, had had in her life. She wrote of her anticipation of getting to meet me and know me. She wrote of her love of reading. She wrote of her church—Presbyterian, as was mine. She had chosen to stay home and raise Chris, her son, as I had for six years while Jim and Tor were young. She told me she, her husband and son had recently moved from Seattle to Cleveland, less than a three-hour drive from where we lived in Ann Arbor.

The doubts and fears John had harbored since the day the letter from Sacramento arrived vanished as soon as he read her letter. Her adoptive mother, for whom this reunion was understandably not easy, had sent an extraordinary gift of pictures of Stephanie from her childhood years going right up to the present. The night we received the letters from each other we made contact through the social worker in Sacramento and talked for an hour and a half by telephone. I didn't sleep the rest of the night.

We met six days later at the home of Liz, who had been my college roommate at the time I found out I was pregnant. She was one of the few people who knew why I left Oberlin, and she lived in Cleveland. Her home was a wonderful place for us to meet and begin to know each other without distractions. Later we went out to eat and then over to her house, where I met her husband Roger and eighteen-month-old Chris.

That summer was a roller coaster of emotions: wonder, feelings of inadequacy, nervousness, an immediate and growing sense of connectedness, joy and sorrow. Once I was swimming and saw a young girl stung by a bee. As she ran to her mother, crying, for comfort, I burst into tears.

Kierkegaard says we can never understand life looking forward, but only looking backward. How fortunate we met just after she and her husband had moved to the Midwest a short drive from us. How fortunate we could easily get together for weekends and get to know each other. How lucky for me that two of her daughters, Zoann and Katherine, were born when I was near.

How fortunate, too, that John came to love her as a daughter and that our sons were at stages in their lives where the surprise entrance of an older half-sister into our family was something they could handle. For Jim, it was the missing piece in the puzzle of why I had left Oberlin, his alma mater as well as John's, so abruptly in the fall of my senior year. For Tor, deep in the first serious romance of his life, it was the first step toward seeing his parents as fellow adults, rather than as paragons.

John and I were once invited to stay with Chris and Zoann while Stephanie, pregnant with Katherine, and Roger had a weekend away to celebrate their tenth wedding anniversary. We felt privileged to be entrusted with them and enjoyed the freedom that comes with being grandparents, secure in the knowledge that, for this one weekend, the disrupted schedules and odd meals were less important than that the children felt comfortable with us and we with them. It is hard to know which couple enjoyed the weekend more. It is certain that I never could have envisioned this weekend the day of my tenth wedding anniversary!

Roger and Stephanie visited us in Ann Arbor and we visited them in Cleveland. My brother Rolf and his family, who also live in Ann Arbor, had us over to dinner to welcome them to the family. Stephanie, who had been raised with only two cousins, both rather distant in age, found she had eight more first cousins ranging from almost her age to twins who are Chris's age.

On our way to Washington, D.C., we stayed overnight with them, and I lamented the fact that we would be farther from them after our move. Within six months Roger had been transferred to Pittsburgh, three hours closer to D.C. They visited us there. We visited them in Pittsburgh. We camped together, ate together, played together, worshipped together, and talked and talked and talked. Now that they have moved back to Seattle, we have the solid foundation of five years of physical and emotional closeness. We continue to exchange letters, telephone calls and visits, even if the visits cannot be as frequent. Having lost her once, I do not want to lose her again.

Looking backward, the years since we were reunited have been a gift beyond anything I could have imagined in those days of sorrow when I first knew I was pregnant. In getting to know her, I have gotten to know myself better. Even now, a gesture of hers, an expression, a reaction sometimes gives me the eerie feeling that I am watching myself. I do not know whether other mothers feel this way about their daughters, or whether I experience it with her only because I have gotten to know her so recently.

Others have noticed the resemblance too. Her brother, Mark, visited us in D.C. with Stephanie and the kids while on a trip home from a two-year stint in Japan. When I first met Mark, he staunchly believed that environment, and not heredity, shapes who we are. As he observed Stephanie and me, however, his ideas began to change. Shortly after their arrival, I asked him, "Don't you feel lonely sometimes just because it is so difficult to talk about complex thoughts and feelings in a foreign language?" Startled, he looked at Stephanie with raised eyebrows. Unbeknownst to me, she had asked him almost the identical question earlier. She responded to his unasked question: "You're the one who said we think alike!"

As I get to know Stephanie better, I appreciate more and more the ways in which we do think alike. She, like me, loves to get to know a new place and learn all about it. She has a keen analytical mind, and, as she talks to me about topics she is puzzling her way through, I recognize the process she is using as being very like the process I use. She loves to read and think and talk about what she reads. She brings the same passionate conviction to the causes she believes in that I bring to mine. Increasingly, I see this dedication in both of us as a reflection of my father's caring for those who most need it.

I have come to have a new respect for heredity. There are strong family resemblances, especially between her children and those of my brother and sister. Chris is the same age as my sister Sonia's second youngest, as well as my brother Rolf's twins, and Zoann is the same age as Sonia's youngest. Put them all together, and they sure look related. It's a contrast to Stephanie's feeling when she was growing up and longed to look like the other people in a family picture.

Beyond physical resemblances, Stephanie just feels like family and has from the first time I met her. At the same time she shows obvious signs of having been raised by loving and caring parents, and I am grateful that my hopes for her, as I said good-bye to her as an infant, were met.

I once was in a group of mothers who had given up their children for adoption. I am lucky that I was allowed to make the decision of whether or not to put my baby up for adoption myself. Some of the women, young girls when they got pregnant, were not given any choice. They carry scars which I do not.

All of us in that group realized that all three parties in an adoption suffer their own peculiar kind of grief. I really cannot imagine the grief her mother must have felt when she learned she could not have her own biological children. Nor can I—family historian that I am—imagine growing up in a family without feeling a connection to my blood ancestors. And I imagine it is difficult for either of them to know the grief I felt at not being able to raise my daughter. I do not know what there is that is so important about that blood relation. To deny its importance, however, only helps mask the grief, rather than accepting and eventually being able to move beyond it.

I am grateful beyond words for the blessings which have been bestowed on me, in spite of my failings and mistakes. I am grateful for the parents who raised Stephanie. I am grateful for their willingness to share her with me. I am grateful to her, her husband and children for including us as part of their family. I am grateful that John was so able to accept her, to love her and to welcome her into our family. I am grateful that Jim and Tor have been able to accept the fact of her existence and to welcome her as a half sister, despite not having known her until they were adults. And most of all, I am grateful to God for how He has held us all in the palm of His hand.

Chapter 8

God

"God has no grandsons or granddaughters."
Catherine Marshall

Greta and I have a few more precious days together. We go on some of my favorite hikes, armed with luxuries I seldom bother to take. We eat her creative and tasty lunches sitting on a blanket. Sometimes, when we come to a particularly lovely spot, we pull out the blanket and sit in comfort while we drink in the scenery. Or we bring books and individual towels so we can sit and read when we find a nice, protected spot in which to curl up. Back at the cabin she cooks, and I effortlessly fulfill my assigned obligation to appreciate the results.

We go swimming in the chillingly cold water in the cove, although not for long, marveling at how much colder the water is than it was in the Gulf. We watch birds from the porch, with Greta delighted to see birds she does not see in her birding jaunts around Minnesota and Wisconsin.

After she leaves, the homey touches she left behind somewhat dull the heartache I feel constantly. Inspired by her, I occasionally fix myself a special meal lit by the candles she brought. I even venture out to church in Cape North one Sunday. The unfamiliarity of the service and the friendliness of the small congregation is more than I am ready for. I do realize, however, that I am overdue for a serious talk with God.

So, the next Sunday, after putting off this discussion for a week, I dig out the hymnal and the Bible I'd packed. I sing: "How Great Thou Art," "Dear Lord and Father of Mankind," "Morning Has Broken," "Is It I, Lord?" I stumble over the last one, even though it is usually one of my favorites. I begin to realize how angry I am and know that it is time to have a real heart-to-heart with God.

"God, how could You do this to me, to us? I've worked so hard to be a good servant to You. *Why* have You rewarded me with this life of one crisis after another?" I rail, suddenly striking the table hard with both my clenched fists. The anger and bitterness that have been building deep within me for all these arduous weeks is finding its way to the surface at last. "Why couldn't we have grown old together? We'd just begun to really have fun. What's the matter, we're not supposed to have *fun*? I don't believe that! Why couldn't we have had some time and warning to prepare for John's death? Why couldn't You have taken me first?" My Norwegian self-con-

trol is slipping rapidly from me, but I just don't care any longer. "How am I supposed to go on living? Is this all there is going to be from now on? This—this emptiness? I don't believe that's Your will for me—how can I do anyone any good in this state? I'm just barely getting from one day to the next. If You have bigger plans for me, You're going to have to show me how to get there. Oh, please, please dear God, show me the path I must follow," I plead. "I can no longer find my way."

Gradually, my anger and despair subside and I feel the peace that comes from knowing I am not alone. I sit silently, cherishing the serenity. Whispering, I close my prayer, "Thank You, God, for all the blessings You have given me. Help me to remember that I am not alone and to trust in You."

I end my home service with tears, a cup of tea, and a greater sense of God's presence and comfort than I have felt since the day of John's memorial service.

That afternoon, I take a long, meditative walk to the lighthouse and remember the second great crisis in our marriage. It started innocently enough. The two of us went on a camping vacation shortly after Tor left for college. I was driving and John was navigating. In our family, as I was growing up, someone besides the driver had the responsibility of mapping out and following our route, noticing signs, etc. I was relying on John to do that.

We both knew we were looking for a major turnoff to reach our destination. Somehow both of us missed it, but thought we were on the right route. As I began noticing mountains to our left, I asked John about them. "Why are there mountains on our left? I thought they were going to be on our right."

"Oh, I don't know. There are lots of mountains around here." John obviously was relaxed to the point of sleepiness, and not interested in doing anything about this anomaly. My misgivings grew as the miles passed.

"Well, could you check the map? It just doesn't seem right."

Reluctantly, John dug out the map, sighed and began looking at where we were supposed to be. "Well, isn't this Highway 92?"

"I don't know. I thought you were supposed to be navigating." My tone was remarkably neutral, considering how right I was.

We both began looking for highway signs. Finally, we saw one telling us that this was Highway 309.

"How did that happen?" I asked, again without, I thought, letting a trace of the recrimination I felt tinge my query.

"What do you mean? You're driving," John responded with a kind of controlled irritation that only increased my own.

Sure that he was completely at fault, I bit my tongue, and focused on the practical issue, "Well, what do we do now?"

With furrowed brow and frequent checks out the window for landmarks, he finally said, "We should have turned left about 60 miles back."

"I didn't see any turnoff," I said, in response to the note of exasperation in his voice. Not wanting to get into a fight, I refrained from adding the obvious: that it was his job to watch for the turnoff when I was driving. Again, I forced myself to return to the immediate question, "Well, is there any way we can cut over to the left now without retracing our steps?"

The answer came after more moments of concentration on the map: "No."

So we turned around, and, despite doing our best to laugh it off, soon we were deep in escalating mutual blame.

"Well, how could you fail to see the turnoff? I'd told you you were supposed to turn left on 92. You were driving. Didn't you pay *any* attention to where you were? I always look at the signs when I am driving."

Stung to the quick by this condescending and unfair attack on me as a driver and person, I responded in kind, "Well, what were you doing? I thought you were looking for the turnoff. After all, you had the map. I was relying on you."

By the time we'd gotten back to where we'd missed the turnoff, it didn't really make any difference that Highway 92 took off to the right on a not-very-noticeable ramp that then went under Highway 309. We were well into dredging up all the complaints we had ever had about each other.

"You always think you're so damned superior to me. That's not easy to live with!" By now I had given up all attempts to bend over backward to be fair, and my tone was hotly accusatory.

"What do you mean? You're the one that always thinks you know exactly what I should be doing. I feel like you're always trying to jerk me around."

Unlike most of our disagreements, this argument just would not die. As we drove to our campsite, fixed and ate dinner, went to bed, and dutifully visited the sights we had come to see the next morning, we were incapable of saying anything to each other without fanning the banked flames of resentment. We kept finding new examples of the other's wrongheadedness, unfairness, stubbornness and delusions of superiority. Even when one of us tried to reach out an olive branch, it was used as one more example of the other's wrongs.

I remember staring down into a deep chasm carved by a cascading river over eons and wondering why a chasm had opened up so suddenly between us. I asked myself: Could we ever bridge the chasm? Did I even want to? Even if I did, did John want to? At that moment, I had no idea what the answers were to those questions. I could even imagine pushing John down the steep bank of the gorge and being happy about seeing him disappear forever.

Maybe out of sheer exhaustion, on the way home we began to talk, very gingerly, about why this was happening. It wasn't too hard to figure out that this might have something to do with Tor's departure for college. That forced us to face the extent to which we had grown in different directions over the years. Without the common, day-to-day project of raising children, those differences became starkly unavoidable. At the heart of our divergence was religion and our beliefs about God.

John and I had married in the midst of a period of religious indifference on my part. Deeply religious as a child and active in my church youth group in high school, I had, almost without thought, lost my interest in religion shortly after I got to college. Mother gently encouraged me to check out the churches and church youth groups at Oberlin, but I, without understanding why myself, did so only sporadically and perfunctorily. I never became involved. I was not alone in this. It is a common pattern; I still do not understand it. The closest I can come is to postulate that it is a stage which some of us go through in the process of developing a mature faith.

John, a minister's son, had a different experience. At first active in religion at Oberlin, where he also attended college, he had, in his sophomore year, experienced what might be termed a religious conversion in reverse. Like Saul, he could describe the exact place it happened—in the shower—if not why. After that he simply could not believe. Only after I returned to the church, did he tell me that he was not merely indifferent to religion, he was an atheist.

My return to faith in God almost twenty years ago was the culmination of the self-searching I had begun after our first marital crisis. My search had led me to Overeaters Anonymous, or OA for short, a program based on the twelve steps of Alcoholics Anonymous. In OA I learned to be friends, to admit weaknesses, to be part of a community and, most profoundly, to look to God. That, in turn, led me to the Presbyterian church, where I found I was hearing different things than I had heard when I was in college. In college I had heard: "Believe what we believe and you can be one of us." After my experience with OA I heard: "Join us in our search to know God's will for us and for the strength to carry it out." I do not know whether that is because what was being said was different or because I was hearing it through different ears.

During this time, God's comfort, mercy and compassion became real to me. I felt burdens dropping from me that I hadn't even known I was carrying. As I realized my only responsibility was my own little part of what I visualized as a gigantic, smoothly working machine of a world, I experienced a new lightness of spirit. When I took my mistakes to God in prayer, I found the compassionate understanding and forgiveness I couldn't give myself. Our little balcony off the spare bedroom became my chapel. Out there I felt God's presence in the trees, the sky, the wind and the changing seasons, times of day and night, cold and warmth. God became the center of my existence, the most important relationship in my life. Discovering and carrying out His will for my life became my life's goal.

During this entire time, our marriage was improving. We became partners instead of two hostile camps. Although we brought different perspectives to parenting, we came to respect the fact that, by sharing our viewpoints, we would come up with more effective strategies than if we decided how to handle problems individually. John liked the changes he saw in me which made me a more loving wife, a better mother, a better homemaker and an easier person to live with. If religion was an important part of those changes, fine, but, to him, it was still all hocus-pocus.

We began to realize on that long car trip back home that our differing views on religion were behind our explosive arguments of the last two days. I was profoundly upset by his dismissing the most important relationship in my life as "hocus-pocus." To me this was a negation of my value as a human being. Without the positive experiences and demands of parenting to hold us together, why should I put up with this attitude? John's dilemma was the mirror image of mine: how could he respect someone whose core beliefs were those he had rejected as rank superstition?

We agreed that we needed an objective, wise third party who could help us see if we could find a way to live together in mutual respect while holding such varying beliefs. We found an understanding counselor, and poured out our concerns. He helped us find ways to recognize we had more in common than we realized. Both of us loved to walk, to sail, to glory in nature. We began to realize that when I talked of feeling close to God during such experiences, John felt much the same, but expressed it as feeling in harmony with the universe. Our counselor encouraged us to walk, to talk, to read and discuss a book on family dynamics. He encouraged us by pointing out what he observed about our deep concern for each other—something he did not often see in couples he counseled.

Slowly, gradually we came to develop a new respect for each other and a new respect for what we shared in spite of our differences. That was ten years ago. Only once since then did we have a serious disagreement, and that was the one simmering when I got the letter about Stephanie. Although it seems almost trivial in retrospect, it did not seem trivial at the time. The issue was whether John loved me enough to find some way to honor me, the mother of his children, on Mother's Day. Or was his firmly held belief that Mother's Day was to be snubbed—as a conspiracy on the part of Hallmark and the candy makers—more important than his love for me?

How patterns repeat in families! It was when I was going through the box of letters during Greta's visit that I had come across a letter to me from my father. It spoke of how fresh and green things looked after a thunderstorm and of how inviting the house looked, thanks to some recent ministrations on Mother's part. The last paragraph read:

> To put topping on my contentment I had Mom read your Father's Day letter to me. That letter has changed my attitude toward Father's Day. It isn't just for the retailers.

But I didn't remember that letter at the time John and I were arguing. It probably wouldn't have helped if I had. Relief came from a totally unexpected source. In the middle of our argument, which had by then lasted for days, the letter from Sacramento arrived saying my daughter was trying to contact me.

Somehow, in working through our complex and somewhat conflicting feelings about the contact from Stephanie, the Mother's Day argument was resolved. I don't remember just how, but I do know that it was never an issue again. It is perhaps significant that part of dealing with our feelings prompted by the arrival of the letter was my coming to respect his fears about the effect an unknown daughter might have on our sons and his coming to respect my strong feelings that if my daughter wanted to get to know me, wild horses would not keep me from her. Again a counselor, this time from Catholic Social Services, helped us to see how completely normal and valid each of our feelings were.

From that time on I do not remember a single instance when we had not been able to share our feelings with each other in the complete confidence that we would be understood and supported by one another. We truly had been best friends, as well as lovers and parents. John would come to church with me on Christmas, Mother's Day and Easter, but never changed his beliefs. I left the relationship between him and God in God's capable hands.

A few years ago we had a long, leisurely evening with friends from church who had recently become neighbors as well. We all talked freely about our histories, our feelings, our triumphs and our trials. Afterward, as Annabelle and I were walking home together, she, a very discerning woman, said to me, "I assume you know, don't you, that John is one of the most spiritual people I have met?" I never told John that, and I was never sure exactly what had led her to the conclusion, but it rang true. Truly I was blessed with a wonderful life's companion and a marriage that aged well. But I hadn't been ready to lose John.

I remember thinking at the age of thirteen that no human being could ever love me with the perfect love that God could. Therefore, I made a soon-forgotten vow to depend solely on God's love, and not to rely on the love of a mere human being for my sense of self and self-worth. To the extent I had remembered it, I had considered it to be the childish promise of a girl on the brink of maturity, who was still afraid of love in the earthly world.

In the years since then I have come to believe that we can know God's love fully only when we experience it through the love of others. Strangely enough, then, John's love and support for me had strengthened my sense of being loved by God. His death has shaken my relationship with God as well as leaving this aching void in my daily existence.

No wonder I have been avoiding God since the memorial service. At least now I feel I have begun to acknowledge that aspect of my loss. Maybe this will mean I can at least be open to ways in which that crucial relationship can be restored and renewed.

Chapter 9

Jim

Jim is screening my mail for me. Since I'd closed down my law practice and taken a leave of absence from all my volunteer activities, I'd asked him to hold most of it for me until I am ready to pick up those reins again. Assuming I will ever be ready to do so. I'm not even getting a newspaper. I am having enough trouble dealing with my internal world, without dealing with all the problems of the external world. And, since all the newspapers I see on my infrequent trips to the store are Canadian, I'm not even tempted by the newsstands when I do pass them. I have no TV and no e-mail and rarely listen to the radio I've brought with me. So it doesn't bother me that Jim has explicitly disclaimed any responsibility for keeping me informed of world or local events.

But he knows me well. So, when he sends news of the annual General Assembly of the Presbyterians, I devour it. As usual, the report is mixed. It is bleak about the issue on which I have spent so many hours and into which I have poured not only effort, but also emotion. Little did I think fifteen years ago that I would care so much about the efforts within my denomination to gain full acceptance of our gay and lesbian members. Little do you ever know, when you have children, where they will lead you. Or where God will lead you. As my minister told me when I returned to church, "If you're really turning your life over to God, hang on, because you are in for a ride!"

This particular ride—what I might call the "gay ride"—began eleven years ago. Jim had just finished his sophomore year at college. John and I had driven from Ann Arbor to Oberlin to pick him up and attend a Kingdon family reunion. Two of Jim's cousins were graduating, and the family clan—many of whom are Oberlin graduates—came from all over the country to celebrate. Since it was also John's 25th class reunion, we had a festive and busy weekend, filled with reminiscing, catching up on news of family and friends, and just enjoying each other's company.

Graduation was Monday morning, Memorial Day, followed by a hectic rush as the students and graduates packed up, the families sorted themselves out and we all said our good-byes. As we were in the process of helping Jim load some things of his into his aunt's car to take them to where he would be staying, having taken a job at the computing center for the summer, he presented me with a totally unexpected question: "Mom, what do you think the Bible says about homosexuality?"

Somewhat distracted by the task at hand, I responded, "I haven't really thought much about it."

"No, really, Mom, what do you think?"

By now, we had squeezed into the back of the car as my sister-in-law drove it to his new house. I reflected a moment. This was the same son who had asked me one Sunday after church, as I, a working mother, was doing the laundry, what I thought was meant by the Biblical injunction to honor the Sabbath and keep it holy. He was serious then and I knew he was serious now.

Then, I'd been able to answer easily. I explained that, while I'd love to be able to devote Sundays to worship, it just wasn't practical—nor required, in my view. What was important, I thought, was not relegating God and worship to an insignificant part of your life, but to make sure God is central in all our activities and to devote time every day to worship, praise, prayer and study of God's will for us.

Now, however, I didn't know how to answer and I didn't know why he was asking. I began to feel a foreboding chill in my heart.

"Well, I don't know, but I suppose it means that people are supposed to seek God's help to overcome any urges toward homosexuality they have." By this time, we had the belongings Jim needed for the summer in his new house, and those he was taking back packed in our motor home, and were returning to Ann Arbor. John was driving, and his mother was in the passenger seat next to him. Jim and I were sitting on the couch in the back, and I was beginning to wish fervently that John were there, too. I already had a feeling I was going to need more wisdom than I possessed.

As Jim began responding, things weren't getting any easier for me. "That's what I tried all through high school. I prayed and prayed and nothing happened. I still felt attracted to other boys and not to girls. I decided not to pray to have my feelings changed in college. It works much better. I feel healthier."

What was Jim telling me? That he was gay? What should I say? Didn't I, as his mother, have a moral obligation to discourage him, whatever that meant? While I had a friend who was lesbian, and that was fine with me, it was different when it was my own son. Was it my fault? What had I done wrong? Was it that I taught him to knit when he was little? And what did he mean about college? What was working better? Was he sexually active? Out of my helter-skelter thoughts, my response was pretty weak, but it was all I could come up with.

"Are you sure? Haven't you ever been attracted to girls?"

"Well, not really. I don't know." Jim was mumbling and not being very articulate himself.

This conversation was not going well. I didn't know what to say. My mind was a jumble of confused thoughts. I couldn't seem to understand what Jim was saying or how to clarify it. And I didn't know how to ask the questions I was really worried about.

Somehow we muddled through the whole three-hour drive, both acutely uncomfortable without getting much further than we had in the first few minutes. I did tell him I loved him. I also reiterated that I thought homosexual feelings were wrong, however right they might seem, and that I would do anything I could to help him surmount them. He said that in junior high and high school he'd thought he was the only person who felt the way he did. In college he was relieved to meet others who had the same feelings and the same experiences of isolation and loneliness.

I didn't cry, not then. Not with my mother-in-law in the front seat. Later, at home, in our bedroom, I cried as I gave John a somewhat incoherent account of our conversation. He was equally devastated, but in his own way. His lack of faith, ironically enough, let him approach the news more compassionately, and he was able to be more understanding than I when he talked to Jim about it the next day.

As John's mother left and my family gathered for its own reunion, I was completely unable to talk with anyone but John about the subject that was continually on my mind—and not much with him. I was too acutely ashamed, hurt, guilty, and grief-stricken. My feelings were raw and confused.

I was sure that I had caused my son's homosexuality. If I hadn't taught him to knit, maybe he wouldn't be gay. If I hadn't loved him so much. If I hadn't made mistakes in raising him. Never mind that I'd loved Tor just as much and had made plenty of mistakes with him. Never mind that Jim had wanted to learn to knit and Tor hadn't. Somewhere I had learned that mothers cause homosexuality, and I was all too ready to blame myself. Even if I hadn't caused Jim's sexual orientation, I was sure that everyone else would believe I had, and that would bring me unspeakable shame. I still thought that being gay was a disorder.

When I wasn't consumed by shame and guilt, I was stricken with a terrible sense of loss. I felt as though I no longer knew Jim, as though he were a stranger who had been substituted for my beloved son. Pictures of promiscuity and wild, hedonistic lives interposed themselves between me and my sober, sensible and shy son. I was afraid for him, and felt unbalanced by the conviction that he would never have the kind of intimate, loving relationship John and I had finally achieved.

I was paralyzed by my feelings and my inability to speak of them—even to God. All God had asked me to do was to take responsibility for my little part of the world, and I had failed in the most important part of that, raising the children entrusted to me.

Jim left to go back to Oberlin before my family left. We only saw him once that summer when we took him and a friend to dinner in Oberlin. John and I talked about it, and almost managed to convince ourselves he was just going through a phase. He was only nineteen, and had never actually used the word gay.

Never once during all that time did I wonder what Jim was going through and how I could help him. I was so absorbed with my own emotions I became unable to be the mother he needed at this difficult point in his life. I didn't realize for years how hurt and surprised he was by my reaction.

It also took me years to see how many signs we had ignored. For instance, we'd had an emotional conversation with Jim the year before when he'd told us he was going to room with a female friend of his. No, they weren't romantically involved, he'd said. When I said I didn't think that was a good idea because of the inevitable temptations, he'd responded in an uncharacteristically tearful voice that it wasn't like that at all. We'd puzzled over the meaning of his tears, but he wasn't saying any more, so we dropped the subject. Now it made more sense and the question was why we couldn't see what is so obvious in hindsight.

At Christmas both Jim and Tor visited us in Palo Alto, where we were spending the year. We talked more. It was clear that this was not a passing phase when he and Tor went on a double date with a friend of Jim's from college and his sister. Jim and Tor also talked—though mostly about our reactions. The fact that Jim was gay was not news to Tor and not a shock. Tor had worked for a gay stage manager in summer theater. Vic was a great boss. Early in the season he had called all the apprentices together and announced that he was gay. Rather than have them hear rumors, he wanted to tell them himself. He had a partner, who had stayed behind at their home in Vermont. If any of them had any questions, he'd be glad to talk to them. After that, it was no big deal to any of them.

Jim and Tor had been close all through their growing-up years. They were only twenty months apart in age and two years apart in school. Tor has said since then he had known that Jim was gay in high school without even knowing he knew. Jim has said it was just taken for granted between Tor and him. There was no need for any discussion.

But John and I continued to struggle with it. I remember sobbing all through Christmas Eve services in Pasadena where we were visiting one of John's brothers and his family. Again, we did not feel ready to discuss it with family. Ironically, his brother's older daughter is lesbian, although we did not know that at the time. He could have helped us.

Tor left Palo Alto before Jim did. The night before Jim left, the three of us had our first discussion about his being gay. If discussion is the right word. I cried as I asked Jim how this could happen when we had such a happy marriage and were such a close-knit family. He cried as he agreed, but said that had nothing to do with it—a point I didn't appreciate or understand at the time. John's voice, while not tearful, expressed his pain as he struggled to understand how this could have happened. It was a difficult night for all of us as we talked without communicating.

The next morning—and John's voice would get husky with unshed tears every time he told this story—John drove Jim to the airport. He said to Jim, "If we've done anything to bring you pain, Jim, we're very sorry."

Jim replied clearly and firmly, "If you're asking me to forgive you, Dad, there's nothing to forgive."

As John observed many times since that conversation, Jim was wise beyond his years. He was saying, "Dad, there's nothing wrong here, so you've done nothing wrong." But we couldn't see that at the time.

Unhappily certain that, yes, Jim really was gay, and unable to turn to family for help, I turned to strangers. After that emotional Christmas I looked up Parents, Families and Friends of Lesbians and Gays (PFLAG) in the phone book. I didn't know much about the organization, but I had read about it in a Dear Abby column years earlier. A wonderful Presbyterian couple who were members of PFLAG visited us in our home and spent several hours listening to us, sharing their experience and lending us books which they had found helpful. Out of all that came from that visit, perhaps the most important was just seeing how they accept their gay son as he is, and how it is no longer painful to them that he is gay. He is a lawyer, and living a happy, productive life with a partner who is a valued part of their family.

We attended a PFLAG meeting where we met other parents, as well as gay men and lesbians. At first we were a little uncomfortable being in a group which included non-heterosexuals. As we went around the group and shared our concerns, however, it became clear that we were all worried about the same things. We all, in one way or another, were trying to figure out how to get through the shock most families experience when they learn that one of their members is gay, bisexual, lesbian or transgendered. I was deeply touched by the loving care with which the gays and lesbians in the group considered how to help their mothers and fathers understand and be able to accept their children for who they are.

We also avidly read the books the PFLAG couple had lent us. I carefully read and studied the few Bible references which are cited over and over again as condemning homosexuality. I read varying interpretations of those passages and books that looked at the issue of homosexuality in the larger context of Jesus' two great commandments:

> "You shall love the Lord your God with all your heart, and with all your soul, and with all your mind." This is the greatest and first commandment. And a second is like it: "You shall love your neighbor as yourself." On these commandments hang all the law and the prophets. Matthew 22:37-40 (NSRV).

I concluded that the Bible does not say much about homosexuality. What it does say is ambiguous, even in its original context. It certainly does not directly address the kind of committed relationship Vic had told Tor about or that our neighbors Paul and Darryl have.

I also read the Kinsey Report and other more factual accounts of homosexuality. I began to think that we were not responsible for Jim's homosexuality. Sure, we made mistakes in raising him, but what parent hasn't? We made many of the same mistakes in raising Tor, and he isn't gay. I searched the psychological literature. No scientific study has ever shown a correlation between parental characteristics or child-rearing mistakes and homosexuality.

John read, too, although not the religious books. We talked. Our thinking evolved. The hypothesis that homosexuality is like an addiction just did not seem to hold up. Instead it is more like left-handedness—something with which certain people are born, which can never really be successfully changed. John, as the son of a left-handed mother, whom everyone had tried to convert to right-handedness, knew how much of a struggle that was, and how unsuccessful efforts to change her basic orientation were. Sure, she learned to do some things with her right hand, but she never became right-handed.

I talked to a neighbor who had gone through a period of wanting to be lesbian for political reasons, but whose feelings made it perfectly clear that, despite her beliefs, she was firmly heterosexual. I talked to people who had grown up on farms and had observed same-sex sexual behavior in animals. If it occurred in nature, how could it be unnatural?

Finally, I came to a point where I realized that Jim's sexual orientation is part of how God created him. I sometimes speculate on God's purpose in making some people gay, lesbian, bisexual or transgendered. Are these just mistakes on his part? I doubt it. I certainly do not feel that Jim is a mistake of God's! I sometimes ponder whether homosexuality is part of God's plan to slow down overpopulation. Maybe it is even a way to provide more loving homes for children who would otherwise have trouble finding adoptive homes. I know of a number of gay and lesbian couples who have adopted "difficult-to-place" children. Or maybe it is just an expression of God's wonderful creativity and a challenge to us to learn to accept those who are different from us. Ultimately, of course, I can't know and do not need to know God's purpose.

There are a lot of things I do not understand about God's creation, and, fortunately, I had already come to a point of realizing that I do not have to understand everything long before I knew Jim was gay. In fact, it had come as, and still is, a great relief to realize that all I have to, and, indeed, all I *can* be responsible for, is my little cog in God's great wheel of creation. That, in fact, gives me plenty to do!

I still felt for a time, however, that, while it wasn't wrong for Jim to be attracted to other men, any expression of this orientation was wrong. I went to a Catholic priest, expecting him to reinforce my conclusion. He listened to me. He listened to my description of what a close family we are and how we had tried to raise Jim in a loving family. I told him how important my relationship to my husband was. Then he simply asked: "Do you think God intends your son to be without the kind of committed, loving relationship you and your husband have? Because, if your son is to have such a relationship, it will be with another man."

This set me back on my heels and made me think anew. With the help of my therapist, I was eventually able to realize that a lot of my reaction against gay sex was visceral, and I ultimately could not support it with reason. The fact that gay sex seems unnatural to me simply means I am heterosexual.

In the meantime, I had to get to know my own son again, without the filter of my perceptions of what it meant to be gay. He was still the same smart, funny, family-oriented person he always had been. In fact, without the burden of struggling against his nature, he was much more fun and much easier to get along with. In earlier years I used to say jokingly that I thought his birth plant must be the cactus—and not just because he loved the ocotillo and other cactuses we encountered on our trip to the desert east of San Diego. During those years, his personality was also prickly. It is not too hard to see why he put up defenses. In recent years, that has been a wholly inept description. In fact, my very conservative and fundamentalist brother-in-law Eric characterized him recently as a "teddy-bear."

At one point I went through a period of fear about AIDS. Fortunately, Jim is without a self-destructive bone in his body. He has always been a person who knows what is right for him, regardless of what other people tell him. I knew I did not need to worry about his getting involved with drugs, alcohol or smoking. When the kids had parties at our house, Jim always made it clear that if anyone wanted to smoke, they would have to go outside to do it, even when it was a bitterly cold winter night. He still does not even drink caffeine, much less alcohol, and does not need or use mind-altering drugs. His life is healthy in every sense of the word. He is still my cherished first-born son, and, as we have accepted him as he is, he has blossomed.

I have had to accept that I let my son down at a time when he was vulnerable, just as my mother let me down at a time when I was vulnerable. Seven years ago, as Mother was facing her failing me, I was facing my failing Jim. While I hope he has always known that I love him, no matter what, I wish I could have listened more and judged less when he first told me of his sexual orientation. I wish I could have reacted with more compassion for what he had gone through. I wish I could have seen the connection then between his moodiness, prickliness and depression in his high-school years and his struggle with what were then nameless feelings that separated him from his friends. I wish I could have empathized with him about the burden he had been carrying alone for years. I wish I could have helped lighten that burden, instead of adding to it.

Chapter 10

The Promise Keepers Are Coming

On my next trip into town, the community is abuzz with talk of a big Promise Keepers rally coming to Halifax. At the Co-op and the laundromat it seems everyone is talking about it. Opinions flow freely. It's a good, healthy Christian movement. It's a cult. It's anti-woman. It's about time someone told men to stand up and take responsibility. It's the best thing to happen to the family since the end of World War II. Bill McCartney, the founder, is a gift from God. He's dangerous. It is a wonderful blessing to have them coming to Canada, and about time! Why didn't they just stay in the States where they belong? The States are full of religious kooks.

I listen, smile, nod my head, and avoid the temptation to be drawn into the discussion. I've been through this before. When the Promise Keepers held their big rally on the Mall in D.C., the offices, churches, newspapers and streets were full of talk about PK, as it became referred to. Then, as now, I agreed with parts of what I heard from many people, but no one really expressed my views. When even my friends did not readily understand my position, why should I try to explain it to strangers? I am quite sure the townspeople can and will come to their own conclusions without my help.

I can't think about PK without thinking about the context in which Bill McCartney started it. He was an assistant football coach in Ann Arbor before he went to Colorado to coach football there. As a good Michigan fan and a person fascinated by people, I had observed the pressures and temptations faced by athletes who become stars at big universities. As our kids grew up and we grew older, I was struck again and again by the youth of these athletes. What a dangerous combination! So many of them had promising careers ruined because they couldn't resist the temptation of readily available drugs. Lives were ruined by the abuse of alcohol and by casual sexual relations.

Often these were young men who were far, far away from the environment in which they were raised and in which they had their roots. Far away in a geographic sense, and far away in a social and cultural sense. I admire Bill McCartney's attempts to reach athletes and other men with a message that they are loved by God, and, because of this, they have a responsibility to God, to themselves and to the people with whom they have relationships. They have a responsibility for the children they father. They have a responsibility to the mothers of their children. I admire Bill McCartney for fostering a sense of male camaraderie based, not on drugs or adulation or a sense of self-importance, but on a right relationship with God and the human need for mutual support in their commitments to keep their promises. I admire his attempts to reach across racial barriers.

I also could not think about Promise Keepers without thinking about Stephanie's husband, Roger. He is a big fan of PK, and I am a great fan of his. If PK helps him to be the admirable husband, father, employee and church leader that he is, it must be doing something right.

As it had been in D.C., some of the talk I hear about PK is from women who are worried that the rally is an attempt to force them back into roles of subordination. Some complain bitterly at being excluded. Some fret that their husbands will come back from the rally refusing to do any of the chores they have gradually taken on.

Again, I nod and listen without expressing an opinion. I have enough respect for the complexity of relationships within marriage and for the inadequacy of language in describing marriages that I have no desire to be drawn into any debate on the subject. Of course, there are different ways of talking about marriages and different ways of thinking about roles within marriage. But I'm not so sure these differences in descriptions tell you much about the quality of those marriages.

In our family, for instance, Greta and Rolf and I all describe our marriages as partnerships. Only in jest did I tell John, "Your wish is my command." And yet all three of us listen to our spouses, love them and want what is best for them. All of our marriages are—were, in my case, I think with a sudden lump in my throat, as I change laundry loads—marked by a mutual gentleness that I really like to see in action. None of us would insist on having our way if doing so would hurt the other. None of us would make important decisions without consulting the other. All of us help out with whatever chores need doing at a particular time.

Sonia and Stephanie are more likely to talk about their marriages in terms of the husband as head of the household. Stephanie contrasts her current view with that of an earlier time when she felt it important to insist on her equality. She knows their marriage is better now and she is happier. But neither Eric, Sonia's husband, nor Roger would dream of insisting on having his way simply because he is the head of the household. Instead, they always talk over big decisions with their wives and seek to make the best decision they can in God's eyes for themselves and for their families. In practice it doesn't look very different from the marriages we describe as partnerships.

So I am not troubled by the messages I hear from PK telling men to take their position as head of the household. Far better that than the abdication of responsibility that happens all too often, whether in the name of freedom or of career-building.

No, the message I worry about from PK is not what they have to say about the role of women. I also know that Bill McCartney is active in Colorado in the political arena, primarily for his efforts to deny homosexuals the civil rights the rest of us enjoy. I shudder at the thought of sending that message to all those good husbands, brothers, fathers and sons. Surely there are gay men and family members of gay men and lesbians in the audience. I was happy that, as far as I could tell, no one addressed the subject of homosexuality from the podium at the D.C. rally. I hope that this was a harbinger of things to come. I was also glad to hear the speakers at the rally urging men to be active in their home churches. And I was glad to hear that the day before the rally the speakers gathered together to pray for God's guidance.

For I have come to believe it is only by praying together for God's guidance that those of us who are religious will be able to resolve the divisive issue of how we, as religious people, treat our gay, lesbian, bisexual and transgendered members. Raised to be a peacemaker, and with a strong personal interest, it is very difficult for me to see my denomination being threatened with a split over this issue. Unfortunately, despite sincere efforts to bridge the chasm between the two sides, all too often positions harden and the chasm grows deeper. It is a battle and likely to remain so for quite a while.

Loving my son as much as I do, knowing how important religion was to him during his junior and senior high school years, and caring as much as I do about my church, I could hardly stay aloof from the battle.

Seven years ago the question of how to treat gays was being hotly debated in the Presbyterian church. A national task force had studied the topic of human sexuality and issued a report. I ordered a copy of that report, which came while Jim was visiting us in Ann Arbor. We both read it the week of his visit. Among other things, it recommended evaluating gay sexual and romantic relationships on the basis of their quality, and not just prohibiting them. We both agreed with those conclusions, although we lamented the clumsy way the report was written. It was verbose or, as Jim put it, "overly redundant." More seriously, it was not specifically grounded in the Bible and Presbyterian history and traditions, although the views expressed grew out of that background.

As Jim's vacation was coming to an end, he decided to ride his bike from Ann Arbor to Boston, where he was then living. He wanted a bike there and I think he also wanted some time alone to think about his job and future career directions. It took him three weeks. During that time we hardly heard from him.

I was worried and upset about his failure to keep in touch, especially since we had such good talks while he was home. In fact that vacation was the first time we had talked easily about the subject of homosexuality.

My imagination ran away with me. I could see him run over or off the road by some bicycle-hating trucker, or beaten up by someone who hated men with long hair. Or maybe he'd gotten into an argument with someone he met about political or social views. As each day went by with no news, I became more and more worried. My worry mutated into anger. How could he possibly not know that we were concerned about his welfare: Had we raised a thoughtless son? Or was he, consciously or unconsciously, acting out of anger at me for the way I had initially reacted to the news of his being gay? I had to acknowledge he had every right to be angry and he could, just as I could with my mother, choose to avoid a close relationship with me.

Finally, we heard from him by e-mail. He was visiting a friend in Oberlin for a few days. It only infuriated me more that he seemed completely oblivious to the notion we might have the slightest concern about his safety and well-being. In the heat of my anger, I sat down and composed a reply:

It was nice to hear from him. We'd been worried about him and I didn't know how to explain his failure to let us know he was all right. I could only think of three possibilities: he was thoughtless, he was acting out of unexpressed anger toward me, or he didn't care about my feelings. I ended the letter by saying, "I love you too much to let our relationship slip away without fighting for it."

I let John read the letter before I sent it; he strongly advised against sending it. John thought I had, as he put it, "knee-capped" Jim. I sent it anyway. My intention was to confront him as a loving mother, and I hoped he would understand that. Jim responded coolly, saying it hadn't occurred to him we'd be worried, asking what there was to worry about, and saying that fighting for our relationship wasn't likely to improve it. Oh, and he was leaving his Oberlin friend's place and wouldn't be back in touch until he reached Rochester in a week or ten days.

I let the issue go, leaving it in God's hands. I knew Jim would need time to decide whether to forgive me and to decide what kind of relationship he wanted with me.

By the time I reach this point in my musings and memories, I am almost back at the cabin. As I carry the sweet-smelling, freshly washed clothes in and put them away, I find myself wondering if my e-mail messages were as harsh as John thought they were. At least in intention, I know they were loving, but how did they actually read?

I pull out the black attaché case that still has the sticker from Mother's real estate firm on the side. It was handy when I was packing, and I put all the old family letters from my desk into it. Resisting the temptation to look at all our old family Christmas letters, I thumb through them until I come to copies of the e-mail messages. Reading them, I realize why John was unhappy that I sent them.

Yes, I was responding out of love and concern, and a fierce desire to maintain contact with my son. But, reading between the lines in my message, I could feel again the hurt because Jim hadn't thought of *my* feelings. Lurking closely beneath that were the twin fears he really didn't love me, and one of the most important relationships in my life could become meaningless. Glancing at the dates, I realized this crisis with Jim was happening the same time as my crisis with Mother. Wow! I'd forgotten that. Two of the four most important relationships in my life in jeopardy at the same time. That makes it a little easier for me to forgive myself for, once again, focusing more on my own needs and feelings than on Jim's. Still, even in retrospect, it is not easy to see myself behaving childishly toward my son.

I chew over these unpalatable thoughts as I fix dinner and take it out on the porch to eat. It is a lovely evening. Clear and cloudless, the immense, peaceful sky and the changing shadows of evening calm my spirit. I had tried to do what was right. I think I have made amends to Jim in the years since that tumultuous period. And even though we never discussed our exchange of letters, it was afterwards that our relationship gradually but steadily improved.

As the sky darkens and the stars begin to come out, I remember what happened in the denomination as the task force report Jim and I had read and discussed was considered. Even before it was readily available to us Presbyterians, a flood of negative publicity about it hit the public press. I was hurt by the readiness of friends in my church to rail against the report when they had not even read it. I found virtually no support within the church I loved so, and was unable to speak, in that atmosphere and at that time, about my own experiences. I was disappointed, but not surprised, when the report was defeated at that year's General Assembly of the Presbyterian church by a vote of 95% against and 5% in favor. Gradually, I became more willing and able to come out myself as the parent of a gay son. That fall a small group of us in the church studied the report and were able to talk about it dispassionately. Our minister was supportive and understanding.

At the same time the Ann Arbor City Council was considering an ordinance to recognize domestic partnerships. While it was not limited to gays and lesbians, it was of greatest importance to them. Unlike heterosexual couples, they did not have the option of marriage. This ordinance provided both a symbolic recognition of their committed relationships and a first step toward some of the benefits enjoyed by married couples. There were letters of fierce opposition sent to the editor of the *Ann Arbor News* and stories that busloads of Christians were coming from Toledo to testify against the ordinance.

John and I both spoke in favor. He spoke as a professor and the father of a gay son. I spoke as a Christian and the mother of two sons, one gay and one straight, who hoped that both of them would have the same right to societal recognition and support of their intimate relationships. This was the first time we experienced the phenomenon of gays and lesbians coming up to us and thanking us for our support, often with wistful expressions of how much they wished their parents could do the same. The first time we marched in a Gay Pride parade we were touched by the applause PFLAG received and by the tears we saw along the route. It is so sad to see these young women and men placed in the position of choosing between their parents' approval and being able to be themselves.

As a Christian, I am always troubled when I go to PFLAG meetings and hear, over and over again, "I know my parents could never accept my being gay *because* they are so religious." Only once have I heard anyone say, "When our daughter came out to us as a lesbian, I was prepared for it because of my church." That dad is a member of a Congregational church that had shared its building with a Metropolitan Community Church made up largely of gays and lesbians. He had come to know many of them over the years as they shared social and spiritual events, and knew that being lesbian is perfectly normal for many women.

Over the years I have noticed how often committed gay couples have supportive parents. One of my co-workers had a gala holy union ceremony and reception put on by his large, extended and very Catholic family. They were obviously delighted with Don, his partner, Sam, and the ceremony. As his grandmother confided how proud she was of Don and how much she liked Sam, I could not help but think of those gay men who were written about by Randy Shilts in *And The Band Played On*. Rejected by their families, their churches and their communities, convinced they were sinful, many of them succumbed to a hedonistic, dangerous lifestyle of promiscuity. That, in turn, left them vulnerable when AIDS was introduced into this country. Many, many of them have since died.

How ironic that the same people who decry homosexual promiscuity are also horrified at the thought of same-sex marriage. Having come to know a number of same-sex couples, I just can't see how allowing them to get married would be a threat to my marriage, or how it would in any way violate Biblical teachings. Surely the Bible teaches us to be concerned about the inner truths, rather than the external forms.

It was during this eventful year I told my family Jim is gay. He had told me it was fine for us to do so, and it became clear over time that he would appreciate it if we did. In the midst of my dealings with Mother, I just decided one day it was time to get rid of all painful family secrets. Over lunch I told Mother and my sisters.

Mother reacted the way I wish I could have—with interest, support and curiosity. In the years before her death she maintained her interest in the subject, and even took Jim and me to a church in Minneapolis with a largely gay and lesbian membership. When she was dying, Jim, who knew he probably could not get there before she died, wrote her a note telling her how much he loved and admired her. Her interest in that church was the first of a number of memories he mentioned. We were all touched.

My sister Greta, who is almost as close in age to Jim as she is to me, was not much more surprised than Tor. She said she'd wondered periodically, but it really didn't make any difference to her, except that she was glad at the prospect of meeting some of his gay friends in Minneapolis. She was at a stage just then when many of her friends were busy having babies in the twilight years of their fertility. Balancing new babies with dual careers did not leave much time for friends. New gay friends were less likely to be going through this, and she needed some friends who weren't. Anyway, she and her husband Rich have always been particularly close to Jim. They share interests and enjoy spending time together, and that wasn't going to change one iota.

The subject was more difficult for my sister Sonia, again because of her religion. She and her family are members of a small community New Testament church that preaches that homosexuality is a sin. On the other hand, she has known and loved Jim since he was a baby, and knows he does not fit the common stereotypes of gay men. She knows John was a strong and loving father, and the old myth about absent or distant fathers and too-close mothers producing gay sons is not applicable in our case.

That fall Sonia and I began a long series of conversations about the subject. Some of them lasted long into the night. We exchanged and discussed books and ideas on the subject. We prayed together. While we do not agree on the subject, she has said Jim is lucky to have parents like us, and the whole thing is a mystery to her. I can agree with that!

Discussing it with Stephanie has also been difficult. For one thing, she does not know Jim well. The only painful conversation I have ever had with her has been about how the church should treat gays and lesbians. She has sent me articles, and I have sent her things I have written. I have talked with her friends in Presbyterians Pro-Life, a group that opposes abortion, and also opposes the ordination of gays and lesbians. Her PPL friends and I do not agree, and I know that she agrees with them more than she does with me. Like Sonia, she may never agree with me on this subject. It is gradually getting easier for us to talk about it. I am learning how to think and speak about gay issues without feeling I have to convince her I am right and she is wrong.

When I started a job in Washington, D.C., six years ago and we began the process of moving our household there, even though John continued to teach at the University of Michigan, I began looking for a new church. I had three criteria: opportunities and support for my personal spiritual growth, an opportunity to be part of a racially and ethnically diverse community, and a welcoming place for both my sons and my atheist husband.

Once I'd visited New York Avenue Presbyterian Church, I suspected my search was over. The first Sunday I was there they were beginning an adult education class on welcoming the strangers in our midst. The class focused on Biblical texts about welcoming strangers in the context of the actions of the Presbyterian church toward gays and lesbians, especially with respect to ordination as lay leaders or clergy. I had been ordained as an elder in Ann Arbor. It pained me to think my son could not be ordained without taking a vow of celibacy that was not required of anyone other than gays. Others in the class were as unhappy as I was about the position of the denomination.

I soon saw New York Avenue as one church that lives its welcoming beliefs. I was welcomed into a small group studying spiritual growth, even though I missed most of the classes. They welcomed Jim when he came with me to church. We met avid University of Michigan alumni and people who had known our minister in Ann Arbor. And this was the church of Catherine Marshall during the years of her marriage to Peter Marshall. Catherine Marshall was an author who had deeply influenced me in the early days of my return to the church.

If it is possible to fall in love with a community, then I fell in love with that church, its ministers and congregation. Over the years my affection and respect have only grown. I have had the privilege of being included as a member of a task force studying the issue of how we treat our gay and lesbian members, and being part of a group guiding the congregational study and reflection on that subject.

In the end, New York Avenue's governing body voted unanimously to propose a change in the way we treat our gay and lesbian members, as a denomination, to the national Presbyterian General Assembly. The proposal—known as an overture—would have allowed ordaining bodies (congregations in the case of lay leaders, and regional presbyteries in the case of clergy) to reach different conclusions on whether or not to ordain gays and lesbians on the same basis as everyone else. I had the honor of presenting that overture to our presbytery and participating in its being adopted by a surprisingly strong vote in its favor.

As an advocate for our overture, I attended the General Assembly two years ago in Albuquerque, New Mexico. That was another emotional roller coaster. For a week I spent fifteen-hour days immersed in the issues and the debates. I listened in rapt attention as I heard over a hundred speakers make two-minute presentations each to the committee handling the issue. Alternately they spoke for and against the ordination of gays. They spoke out of their faith, their struggles, their beliefs, their hearts. Everyone was sincere and respectful. Many were sad.

I was deeply moved by what I heard and agreed with much on both sides of the issue. The importance of seeking God's will for our lives, the dangers of self-delusion, the power of prayer, the need to be rigorously honest with ourselves and others, the value of the Bible, tradition and spiritual leaders in discerning God's will—these were all principles with which I heartily concurred. Only when non-gay people asserted that they knew what was right for lesbians and gays did I grow restive and wish I could refute them. What especially irked me were a few people who claimed that gays and lesbians could be "saved" from their "lifestyles." How dare they assume they know what shape salvation is for my son! Mentally, I challenged them to find anything objectionable about his lifestyle, when he is as responsible and moral a person as anyone I know. I almost snorted in disgust.

My overwhelming conviction at the end of the personal testimony was that any one listening to those hours of speeches with an open mind and heart must see this was not a question of who believed in the Bible or who believed in love. People on both sides of the issue obviously were speaking out of belief in God, the Bible and our Presbyterian beliefs and traditions. People on both sides of the issue spoke out of love (or at least professed love) for gays and lesbians.

My heart yearned for us to find a resolution to this dilemma that would recognize the genuine disagreement within our denomination— a way that would not result in one side winning and the other side losing, while still recognizing the equality of all of us, regardless of sexual orientation.

As an overture advocate, I had a few minutes to speak to the committee after the public hearing. I began my statement by saying:

> I embody the tension that exists in the church today. I struggle with this issue on a daily basis at the very personal level of my family for I am the mother of a daughter who is a member of Presbyterian Pro-Life and also the mother of a gay son.

There were more than fifty overtures before the committee. Those who spoke in favor of permitting ordination included Eugene March, speaking on his own behalf and on behalf of a majority of the Biblical scholars at Presbyterian theological seminaries who had signed a document titled "The Whole Bible for the Whole Human Family." This document placed the issue in the context of the larger message of the Bible, and rejected the idea that the Bible precludes the ordination of gays and lesbians unless they are celibate.

That day was a high for me. The next day was a low. Committee member after committee member spoke for "maintaining the authority of Scripture," by which they meant continuing to preclude full acceptance of homosexuals. I felt personally hurt by those comments. Hadn't they heard the strong convictions of those who disagreed with them on Biblical grounds? How could they ignore all of us, including the Biblical scholars? How could I stay in this church which could not even accept that my beliefs were, like theirs, the fruit of my belief in God and the Bible?

And, yet, because of my talks with Sonia and Stephanie, because I had read widely, including books written by those with whom I disagreed, and because I, in some sense at least, consider myself "born again," I could probably understand their point of view better than some. I talked with Stephanie's friends at the PPL booth. I talked with a woman who describes herself as an ex-lesbian healed by prayer. I went to a PPL presentation that featured the story of an ex-gay man, now "healed of his homosexuality" and apparently happily married.

I am a sucker for stories of healing and redemption. You hear them and see them all the time in twelve-step programs. I have felt the healing presence of God in my life over and over again. I am always happy to see that healing happen in the lives of others.

But healing and redemption, for most gays, does not bring about a change in their sexual orientation. I have seen first-hand the hurt that results when a gay person tries to deny his or her sexual orientation and marries. I was always grateful, even in the early days after Jim told us he was gay, that he had not married in an attempt to deny or "cure" his homosexuality. I believe it is the job of the church to bring people closer to God and to do what we can to support His working in their lives. Just what this might mean in a particular life is not always easy for me to say—even when that life is mine.

Oddly enough, the two people I talked to the most by telephone the week I was in Albuquerque were Stephanie and Jim. Stephanie had been to General Assemblies twice before as an observer with PPL and found the process fascinating. She listened intently as I reported on all that happened without offering her opinion on the central issue. And I did not ask.

It has occurred to me that Stephanie, my father and I all have been passionate advocates for those whom we see as needing protection. Because of our life experiences, we have been touched by different groups of people. For Stephanie that group is unborn babies in danger of abortion. As John sometimes said, if I had her history, I might feel the same protectiveness as fervently as she does. It is strange to think, under other circumstances, I might have been the one at the PPL booth, and she might have been the one visiting the Presbyterians for Lesbian and Gay Concerns. Ironically, the two booths are often side by side at General Assembly.

I remember talking to Jim the night before the final vote as Independence Day fireworks lit the sky outside my motel room. He had followed the debate ever since the year we read the task force report. He had advised me, and offered wisdom gained from his general knowledge of the Presbyterian church, the Bible, and gay culture, experiences and struggles. I was cautiously optimistic even though the committee had voted against our overture. A minority report had been drafted that offered yet another middle ground. I was convinced the position of the committee was wrong theologically and morally and hoped the body of the General

Assembly would see it that way. Jim, uncharacteristically for him, closed by saying that he would be praying for us all.

When the vote was announced, 57% of the commissioners voted for the Committee's majority report and 43% against. I had two immediate, powerful, contradictory reactions. First, I was stunned and hurt. Much to my surprise, I joined about a thousand others in marching around the hall, first in silence and then singing, "We are marching in the Light of God." Many were in tears, as was I. Some of those crying had not joined those marching and had worked on behalf of the Committee's majority report.

Simultaneously and paradoxically, I had a fierce feeling of belonging. When I heard that 43% of the commissioners voted against the majority report, I realized: "This is *our* church, too!" Never again would I feel lonely or isolated as the accepting Presbyterian mother of a gay man.

Since coming back from Albuquerque, I have become convinced that lasting, peaceful change will not come in the denomination until it comes in people's hearts. I believe this is most likely to happen person by person and congregation by congregation. On the local level we know that the person with whom we profoundly disagree on this issue has had a lifetime of devotion to the church and shares our interest in peacemaking. This knowledge tempers our discussions, especially when the person knows you are the mother of a gay son. On the other hand, when people learn that the lay leader with whom they have worked and whom they have known for years as a devoted Christian is a gay man and hear of his struggle to accept himself, they look at the issue of ordaining gays differently than they did before.

At this point in my musings, I become aware of the evening's chill. I am cold and stiff from not moving for so long. I get up slowly, stretch, go inside, light a fire and reread the mail sent by Jim more carefully. It offers hope. Maybe some of the grassroots support needed before any kind of a consensus can be reached is building. Maybe, just maybe, our denomination will eventually be able to reach a resolution most of us can accept.

Chapter 11

Trip to the Historical Museum

On a whim one day I decide to stop at the Cape North Historical Society Museum instead of just driving past as I usually do on my way to the Co-op. John and I had stopped there the year before on our way back from Bear Cove. Then there had been a meeting of a needlework group of some kind with four women sitting around a table talking as they crocheted and enjoyed tea and scones together. At first, as we overheard them talking about salt cod, I thought they were a living reenactment of life as it must have been when the area was settled 150 years ago or so. Later, as talk turned to present-day topics, it became clear that was not the case. But since that day I remembered the museum as an especially appealing spot to stop and visit. John, never much of a museum fan, was enchanted as well by the needlework society, but anxious to get on our way, so I relish the thought of going through the museum without a time deadline.

The museum is filled with various possessions saved from those used by the early settlers who came to this area from Scotland. There is also a series of notebooks painstakingly documenting various aspects of life on Cape North over the centuries. There is at least one notebook devoted to the Indians who preceded the Scottish settlers. A pamphlet written by a sailor shipwrecked off Cape North in the 18th century catches my eye. But most interesting to me is the notebook about lighthouses. It includes pictures and historical notes about the lighthouse to which I so often walk. It is easy to see that the history of the lighthouse is interwoven with the history of the family of our campground host, Ken. I remember from last year that he is the seventh generation of his family to live in Bear Cove—although the first generation to run the campground at which we stayed last year. His surname, McLellan, appears more frequently than any other surname in the list of lighthouse keepers.

More recent history is covered too. Of course, the construction of the Cabot Trail in the 1930s, the first road through the wilderness bisecting the island at its northern end, deserves and receives a lot of attention. But I am pleased to see references to the seventeen-mile foot trail more recently built through the roadless forest between Bear Cove and Pleasant Bay. Last year we learned that Ken helped build it over the course of three years of hard work for the Nova Scotia Department of Natural Resources. Again, my curiosity is piqued. How I'd love to hike that trail, but to manage that would take resources I do not have available. My camping things are almost all in D.C., and few of them are suited for backpacking. Besides, I do not want to go on the trail enough to overcome my aversion to carrying a big pack on my back. Nor does it seem prudent to go on my first overnight backpacking trip by myself. Oh, well, it is a nice dream with which to while away an afternoon.

I stop and call Stephanie from the pay phone in front of the Co-op.

"Hi, it's Kirsten. How are you?"

"Oh, hi! It's good to hear your voice." I feel a rush of warmth and affection at hearing her lilting greeting. I haven't talked to her since I left D.C.

"We're doing great," she continues. "So far, it's been a wonderful summer out here. Mom and Mark went with us to stay in a pair of condos near the Columbia Gorge. It reminded us of the visit Roger and I took there last year, but it was fun in a different way with the kids along. We took them to see the Bonneville Dam. They loved seeing the fish climb up the river from the window inside the building. Especially Jo. We could hardly drag her away when it was time to leave."

"Sounds like fun. Wish I didn't live so far away." I hate having so much of my family on the west coast, although I do have to admit that Portland and Seattle seem to be good places for them to live. I especially miss being able to see the kids. Every time I see them, I realize how fast they are growing up and how precious these fleeting years of their childhood are. And while Stephanie's adoptive mother is, and rightfully so, the one all of us refer to and think of as her mother, the kids have accepted me as a grandmother from the time they could talk. Fortunately, no one can ever have too many grandmothers! And, given the reality of divorce and remarriage, they aren't the only children with more than the customary two.

"How's your mother?" I still haven't met her. This is partly because we have rarely been geographically close, but also because it has been somewhat difficult for her to adjust to having me as a part of Stephanie's life. Understandably so. Especially when Stephanie's younger brother, Mark, sought out and found his birth parents, now married and the parents of two daughters, shortly after Stephanie and I met. But she has been working on understanding and dealing with her feelings. I hope that a time will come when she will feel comfortable with the idea of meeting me. We are both animal lovers, both dote on Stephanie's kids, and both love Stephanie. Words cannot express my appreciation to her for all that she has done to make Stephanie the person she is now.

"She's doing well. They may be moving back to eastern Washington, which would be great for all of us. Rural Arizona is not a very easy place to visit, although we had a good time there in March. We had some really good talks on this trip. She is feeling more and more comfortable about you. And about Mark's getting to know his family. Oh, and she especially asked me to send her condolences to you."

"Tell her I really appreciate that." I am surprised and touched. Surprised both at the message and at how much it means to me. "How's Mark?"

"Good. He has a new job. And his sisters are coming to visit him in a couple of weeks." I wonder briefly how Stephanie feels about her brother having sisters to whom she is not related. I know she has met his birth mother, but not his sisters. "He's thinking of bringing them up here so they can see Seattle and we have a chance to meet them. And Mom might even meet them while they are here."

"Hmm. Hope it works out well. It should be interesting. And interesting to explain." On a few occasions I have tried to explain my relationship to Mark: my daughter's brother, to whom I am not related. Now I just refer to him as a friend, unless it is a conversation specifically about adoptive relationships.

"Yes, it should be. But you know the kids. They are always glad to welcome anyone. They don't really care that much about the precise relationship."

"Yes, I remember how eagerly they always welcome Tor." Tor has had several good visits with her family, sometimes when I was there and sometimes when I was not. It's nice for me to know that he has family closer to him than the east coast, especially since his divorce. Last Thanksgiving he and Mark had both been there, and the kids were delighted to have two single uncles to play with them. "They're pretty good icebreakers," I complete my thought.

"That's for sure. Week after next we're going to Orcas Island again with Roger's sister and family. You can imagine how much they are looking forward to that."

"I don't blame them. Sometime I'd like to go out there myself. It sounds like a spectacular place."

"Yeah. I really like it myself. And I always like to get out camping." Funny how much their family likes camping. Camping was one of the things our family did best, both when I was growing up and when we were raising Jim and Tor. We'd had some memorable camping vacations with Stephanie and family, once when they'd lived in Pittsburgh and once with Tor in Mount St. Helens National Monument. "You should come out sometime for a long visit at a time when we can plan to go camping."

"I'm not making any plans yet." True, but the thought of visiting them pulls at me. "Maybe this fall. I don't know if that will still be good for camping."

"Depends. Usually we have at least some good fall weather." Rain is not one of my favorite weather conditions. And, since rain is a staple of the Seattle weather picture, it is fortunate that when visiting Stephanie and family we are not dependent on good weather. "So, how are you doing?"

"It's hard to know." Suddenly I am aware of a lump in my throat and find that I can't go on speaking.

"Every once in a while, I try to imagine what it was like for Roger's mother when his father died at such a young age. Or, worse yet, what I would do if something happened to Roger."

"Well, as far as I am concerned, widowhood is the pits. Especially when you have a wonderful marriage and love your husband and he is also your best friend. It just seems so unfair. Especially when John was so careful with his diet and all. Statistically, he never should have had a stroke, much less died. At least I know we both did everything we could."

"But that's not much help, is it?"

"Nope, sure isn't. I'm trying to see God's will in all of this, but it's pretty hard. I remember the letter Sonia wrote to Mom and Dad when we found out Dad was dying. She said that God is brokenhearted and grieves with us when we suffer. She quoted from Psalm 91, 'and under His wings, you will find refuge.' I still do believe that God works to bring good out of even the most awful situation, and that we learn from our suffering. But, I don't see why I had to learn whatever I am supposed to be learning from this right now. I would rather have waited about twenty or thirty years."

"Well, I don't blame you. We'll miss him too. Chris still talks about his visit to see you last summer and still has moments of feeling really sad about Grampa John's death." I fleetingly recall the day John became Grampa to Chris: the day when he offered to take him to the zoo while Stephanie, Mark, I and then-baby Zoann went to church.

"I'm so glad you and Chris came to the memorial service. You know, John couldn't have loved you—or the kids—more if he'd been your father."

"I'm glad we could come." She hesitates, "He meant a lot to us, too."

"I know," I respond, thinking of the good times John had with her children. "I've probably told you how much Chris enjoyed John reading A.A. Milne poems and Pogo to him. Next time Tor visits, Chris might enjoy hearing him read the poems, at least. I don't know about Pogo. Our books are falling apart and I don't know if any of the libraries around there have them. With John gone, only Jim and Tor can give the genuine Kingdon interpretation."

"We'll have to keep that in mind."

"Well, it's starting to get chilly, and someone is waiting to use the phone. So, guess I better go."

"Me, too. The kids are sounding like they need a little adult supervision."

"I'm glad you were home and had a few minutes. I'm so glad to have you in my life, now more than ever. I love you. Give Roger and the kids a hug from me. I'll call again."

"I will. I love you too. You are in our prayers and thoughts."

"Thanks. That means a lot to me."

Only that night as I sit on my porch listening to the waves and watching the stars do I realize that I am making progress. For an afternoon, at least, I was able to become interested in the lives of other people, both dead and alive, and to contemplate plans and dreams for a future that does not include John. Maybe I am beginning to feel stirrings of a dormant interest in life beyond John's death. It is a bittersweet thought, and I go to bed missing John.

Chapter 12

Walk on Bear Cove Mountain

One step forward and two steps back. The next day I wake up expecting John to be in bed beside me, and feel a visceral sense of loss when I open my eyes and remember. I miss the way we used to snuggle and talk about plans for the day before getting up. The missing of him just seems to get worse as the day wears on. I want to hear his voice while I am fixing breakfast. I want to share breakfast and the view from the porch with him. I want to plan with him what we will do today. I want to tell him about what I learned at the museum and about the news from Stephanie. I want to go out to Seattle and Portland with him and visit Stephanie and her family and Tor. I want to be hugged by him, be held by him, and to feel and experience his love. Today I can't imagine ever being contented again without him.

I flee up Bear Cove Mountain. It doesn't help much. I keep remembering our walk up there last year. I want to share the beauty with him, admire the daisies and reminisce about our last trip together. At least I am moving, however, and at least I sometimes have to think about avoiding obstacles in my path.

As I reach the plateau, I notice movement in the meadow. Curious, I look to see if it is a deer. Nope, too dark, too low to the ground, too slow and lumbering, too bulky. When I realize it is a black bear, I freeze. I am not wearing bear bells and have been walking over a section of the trail which is soft and kind of mossy so I haven't been making much noise. Apparently the bear did not hear me coming. Thoughts crowd my head. Thank God, I left too hastily to bring any food. I hope it's not a mother bear with cubs somewhere behind me. Please, God, keep me from being mauled by an angry or frightened mother bear.

I try to remember what I should do, assuming, that is, that I can ever get my legs, which seem to have lost all strength, to move again. What was it Chris told me last summer? Keep eye contact with the bear and back away? Or is it to avoid eye contact and back away? Anyway, backing up seems like a good idea. I know I can't outrun it and trees offer little help as I am out in the open. Besides, I am pretty sure the bear is better at climbing trees than I am.

Slowly, gradually I back off, being careful both to keep an eye on the bear, who thankfully seems to be blissfully unaware of my presence, and to keep glancing at where I am going so that I do not stumble or fall, thereby attracting the bear's attention. My backward progress seems painfully slow and the woods a long, long ways away. Fortunately, the bear seems to be interested in whatever it is eating. Once it raises its head, sniffs the air, and I freeze

again, profoundly hoping I am downwind of it. I have never been good at figuring out downwind and upwind and never less so than now. After a moment it lowers its head and resumes its munching.

After what seems like hours, I reach the trees. At that point I can't resist turning around and fleeing down the path as silently and swiftly as I can. Although I have a tingling feeling in my spine, I do not see or hear any sign that the bear is following me down.

I arrive home, trembling, and feeling in need of a shot of whiskey. Lacking that, I fix myself a cup of strong tea—of such great help in so many English novels—with shaking hands and pour in milk and sugar. I gulp down the first cup. Gradually my shaking subsides, and I decide to venture to the porch with my second cup. Good. No bears. Just the usual sea, cove, trees, birds and a few boats out on the water.

It's not until later, while I am fixing dinner, that I realize, despite my desolation at losing John, I never thought: oh, well, at least if the bear kills me, my misery will be over. In fact, my body is ahead of my mind. It has no intention of letting me die before my time. I am strangely cheered by this realization. No matter how much I miss John and wonder if my life is worth living, apparently at some level the decision of whether life without him is worth living has already been made.

Chapter 13

Amber

Not long after my encounter with the bear, Sadie stops by to visit. She is accompanied by a dog, whom she introduces to me as Amber. With her coat shading from honey to caramel-colored in the sunlight, it is not difficult to see how she got her name. She reminds me of the precious fragments of amber Chris and I saw on display at the Smithsonian when he visited last summer.

Sadie soon gets to the purpose of her visit. Amber needs a home. She belongs to Sadie's great aunt, Marion, who fell last week and broke her hip. Now she is in the hospital. No one else in Sadie's large family can take Amber, for one reason or another, so she wound up with good-hearted Sadie and Ken. She has been there for a few days and it is clear that it is not going to work. She is used to being indoors and doesn't seem to be adapting to their active, mobile existence, much of it outdoors at and around the campground. If they leave her in the house all day, she whimpers. If they let her run loose, she bothers the campers. Not all of them want to give her the attention and affection she is used to getting. Then, too, she is large and some of the campers mistake her friendliness for threats. Some even threw stones at her to drive her off. While she is good with Ken and Sadie's girls, she isn't really used to being around kids for any length of time, and their activity seems to unsettle her. Would I consider keeping her until Aunt Marion returns home?

I look at Amber more closely. She has the head and silky fur, as well as the coloring and tail, of a golden retriever. But she is smaller than most goldens I have known and her stockiness in the shoulders suggests some German shepherd blood. Despite the tales of her failure to adjust to the campground, she seems perfectly at ease on my porch. She has not pushed herself on me, but welcomes my greeting and friendly head-scratching. Now she is lying next to Sadie looking up at me with questioning eyes.

Always an animal lover, I would have a hard time saying no under any circumstances. The fact that Ken and Sadie found me the cabin, made all the arrangements, take in my mail, take phone messages for me, let me use their phone and are good to me in a million small ways argues strongly in favor of agreeing. Finally, of course, the thought of having a companion on my walks, a companion whose tags would click with every step, a companion who would warn bears of our presence long before a possible encounter—well, that clinches it. So Amber comes to stay with me for a while.

Chapter 14

News from D.C.

"Hi Mom." Jim's voice sounds happy and excited, so I relax, knowing it is not bad news that led him to ask Sadie to give me his message to call him.

"Hi Jim. What's up?"

"How'd you like some visitors?" Hmm. Visitors. Plural.

"I'd love some . . . depending on who they are. Who'd you have in mind?"

"Remember the friend I mentioned whose mother died recently? His name is Derek. I'd like to have you meet each other and we'd both like to see Bear Cove. He teaches and wants to take some time off before classes start. So we thought we'd fly up to Halifax, rent a car and drive up to Bear Cove."

Jim began his dating career late. As with a lot of gays, his adolescence was spent largely in dealing with issues relating to his sexual orientation. Although not nearly as shy now as he was then, he still has a natural reserve that, coupled with his high standards, has kept him unattached past his 31st birthday. Once, as a promising relationship was breaking up, he told us when he met someone he was really serious about, he would want to introduce us and get our opinions. As he said, "You characters know me pretty well and want what is best for me, and I'll want to know what you think."

Now, he is going to have to settle for one parent's opinion. Too bad. I feel a little as I felt when he told me he was gay while John entertained his mother in the front of our motor home. Except now John is a lot more inaccessible. Oh, well, I guess my insight, such as it is, is going to be all Jim will get.

"Sounds great. Any particular ideas about what you would like to do?"

"Well, we thought we would bring our tents. And we'd like to do some hiking." Hmm. Maybe God is showing me a way to fulfill what has been only a dream until now.

"Any interest in an overnight hike?"

"Maybe. Where?"

"Well, there's a seventeen-mile hike to Pleasant Bay through the wilderness I see from Bear Cove Mountain. It goes to Pollett Cove, which looks like a little less than halfway. It also looks like a good place to camp for a night or two. Then it goes down to Pleasant Bay more or less along the coast. I've thought about doing it myself, but I'd prefer to have company. That is, if you want to do it and don't mind having me along."

"Sounds intriguing. Let me talk to Derek about it tonight. Why don't you call me sometime tomorrow? We're thinking of leaving a week from Friday, spending the next week in Nova Scotia and flying back the Monday after that."

When I talk to Jim the next day, he sounds even more upbeat. Derek is enthusiastic about the idea. Eagerly, we make plans. Ken had given me the name of someone who could rent us a pair of pack mules to carry the bulky, heavy stuff. They'd bring the mules to Bear Cove and we could leave them in Pleasant Bay at the end of the trip. I'll arrange that.

Derek and Jim will stay at Chéticamp campground in Cape Breton Highlands National Park, just an hour or so south of Pleasant Bay on Friday night. I'll drive down to meet them at the Rusty Anchor for lunch on Saturday and see if we can leave the rented car in Pleasant Bay at the place where we'll leave the mules so we'll have a car waiting for us at the end of the trip. We'll start out on Monday, weather permitting, and arrive in Pleasant Bay on Tuesday or Wednesday, depending on how long we decide to take.

Then we talk about supplies. I'll call REI's 800 number and order a backpacking one-person tent, making sure it has room for me and Amber. Jim and Derek already have their own backpacking tents and sleeping bags. They'll bring my sleeping bag and mattress and get the cook set and portable stove from the motor home. I'll plan a menu and get the supplies. If there is anything I can't get nearby, I'll let them know and they can pick it up on their way. Jim can't think of anything Derek doesn't like to eat—except artichokes. That won't be too much of a constraint on my menu-planning.

I tell Jim about Amber and about my bear-sighting on Bear Cove Mountain. There's no need for bear bells as long as she has her tags. He is suitably impressed, but not deterred. In retrospect my experience with the bear does not seem quite as alarming as it did at the time. I know bears are shy and generally avoid people, but I also know that they are stronger than I am, a lot stronger. I have heard they can be vicious if they feel cornered or threatened, and that they are not always predictable. In any event, I have no desire to repeat my experience, with or without company.

As I make arrangements, plan the menu and do the shopping, I realize I am actually enjoying myself. I am happy that Jim has found someone he is seriously interested in, and pleased that he still cares about having him meet me. I am really looking forward to the trip.

Chapter 15

Jim and Derek

The morning Jim and Derek are to arrive, I wake up early. Although it is cloudy when I get up, the forecast is for increasing sunshine and sounds good for the whole week. Dinner is going to be easy. I set the table and leave at least an hour early. When I get there, I drive to the trail head, check on the arrangements for leaving the car and the mules, and drive back to the Rusty Anchor.

Although I am still early when I reach the parking lot, I spot the two of them, just getting out of a red Toyota Corolla, Derek on the driver's side. He is taller than Jim, red-haired and handsome. I pull in beside them, feeling surprisingly shy. Jim walks over to me, tucking his old plaid madras shirt very tight in the front, the way he does sometimes when he is in a new situation and doesn't quite feel at ease.

I fumble with my purse, finally hanging it on my shoulder so I can give Jim a hug and a kiss. "So, how was your trip?" I ask, and then wonder if I shouldn't have said something to Derek first.

"Fine," Jim says, awkwardly returning my hug and kiss, while simultaneously turning toward Derek. "Mom, this is Derek. Derek, this is my mom, as you may have guessed." Jim, not usually one for smooth introductions, ends with a smile.

"It's great to finally meet you." I extend my right hand to him.

"Same here," Derek responds with a smile. His handshake is firm and his voice pleasant. Although casually dressed in chinos and a short-sleeved shirt, he looks as though he would fit in anywhere. I relax a bit. So far, so good.

"Well, let's go in. Greta and I ate here when she visited and the Cape Breton fish cakes were as good then as they were last summer." I stop abruptly, feeling as though I am chattering, and remembering my meal here last summer with John. In silence we walk in and find a table by the window. All three of us order the fish cakes and fresh lemonade.

"So, Jim tells me you're a teacher," I say, turning to Derek once the very efficient waitress has left. "But I don't think he told me what or where you teach."

"I teach history at American University."

"Oh, I taught history, too, but in middle school right after we were married." I add ruefully, "It may have been the hardest job I ever had."

"I can imagine," chuckles Derek. "College freshmen can be difficult enough."

Mentally, I register another mark of approval. Maybe it's my own bias, but I can't imagine that Jim would be happy with someone who is not an intellectual. You just don't major in history these days unless you love ideas more than money. I relax a little more. "What's your area of specialty?"

"American." He hesitates, and I nod encouragingly. "Actually, my dissertation is a comparative study of American policy and attitudes toward three minority groups of men: Native American, African-American and gay."

"Sounds fascinating. I'd love to read it. How did you happen to pick your topic?"

"Well, growing up in Wyoming, as I did, I learned a lot about Native American history and culture. Then, in high school my best friend was a Native American. We could really identify with the way each of us felt isolated. Even before I came out as gay, I knew I was different, and our classmates treated me that way, too. Then, in college, once I came out, even my friends, except Ben, changed. You could see that they superimposed ideas of what it meant to be gay on their knowledge of what I was like. I think the idea of a gay friend was just too threatening to them. By thinking of me as 'gay,' instead of as 'Derek,' it made it easier for them to reject me.

"But Ben wasn't that way. Even though he was smart and lived in town, people treated him as though he were dumb and ignorant of modern American ways. Oh, and as though he'd get roaring drunk every night, when he didn't even drink. They were so set in their beliefs that they never even tried to get to know him as I did. Actually, he is one of the most thoughtful, articulate, centered people I know. He really knows who he is and what he believes, so he was able to let a lot of the abuse he got just roll off his back. I learned a lot from him about that and about how to appreciate the world of nature."

"Where is he now?" I like Derek's appreciation of someone who knows himself. Jim has always had that same quality of knowing what is good for him—and what is not—and of not really caring much how other people react to him.

"Ben? Oddly enough, after majoring in forestry at the University of Wyoming, he developed a fascination for gems. He's now in South Africa, with his wife and two children, as a consultant to DeBeers. They love it there."

We are interrupted by the arrival of our lunch, and are quiet for a while as we concentrate on the food. I, at least, am absorbed in the glimpse into Ben's life and in how hard it is to predict where people will wind up when they follow their passions.

"Mom," Jim interrupts my reverie, "did I tell you that Derek's Ph.D. is from the University of Wisconsin? He knows 'Nuckle' Bob." John's oldest brother, known affectionately by our kids as "Nuckle Bob," is a well-known Reformation historian at the University of Wisconsin.

"Well, our paths never actually crossed, but, of course, I heard of him and his work in translating, and making accessible, the old, original Geneva documents from John Calvin's time. Actually, I thought of him when I found some 19th-century, untranslated Navaho documents in the Smithsonian archives. Fortunately, I was able to find a Navaho translator who helped me figure them out. They turned out to be quite useful in showing how very differently the Navaho and the U.S. government viewed the purpose and intended effect of the same treaty."

When the check comes, both Derek and I grab for it, but I insist on paying. John planned well for the future, and I know I am better able to afford the meal than either of them, especially since they've already put out a lot of money for the air fare, the car and equipment. Still, I am pleased that Derek offers and genuinely seems to want to treat me. I assure him that I'll let him pick up the tab the next time we eat out, which will be after we finish our hike.

After lunch we drive up to the trail head, where we leave the rental car, and all ride back in my Taurus. On the way they regale me with stories of how they'd coped the night before in the dark and rain with new camping equipment and a lantern that wouldn't light. Since they'd both managed to get dry and stay dry for the night, and sleep well, it's easy to laugh about it now in the sunshine, which has come out while we were eating. By day, it was also easy to see what they'd been doing wrong with the lantern. They'd tested it this morning, so we know we have a working lantern for the trip.

As we approach Bear Cove, they are suitably impressed by the steep cliffs, green interior and blue sea. We decide to take advantage of the perfect afternoon to climb up Bear Cove Mountain. I haven't been up there since my encounter with the bear and am glad to have company, including Amber, who'd welcomed us all on our arrival back at the cabin. Her tags are comfortingly audible in the quiet afternoon. I, at least, have no desire to surprise the bear again. Neither do my very sensible visitors. The experience has made me appreciate John's caution and insistence on buying and using bear bells in a way I hadn't while he was alive. I send a quiet, mental apology heavenward.

Derek and Jim stop in awed silence at the top where you can first see the river valley and unbroken woods into which we will be heading. We then turn to the right, walking up the plateau toward the ocean where we see the campground and the cove, including the patch of woods that surrounds my hidden cabin. But we are all more interested in the view toward Pleasant Bay. Even though I have brought only a sketchy map of hiking trails in the area, we are able to see the terrain we will be following for the first part of the hike. It looks very appealing. Nothing but dense woods, with no signs of human habitation.

After dinner we sit on the porch, sipping herbal tea and watching the dusk turn to starlight. Derek talks a bit of his childhood growing up on a Wyoming ranch near Cheyenne. He tells of horseback rides with his father to check the cattle put out to feed in the foothills of the Rockies and of sitting on the front porch swing with his mother watching the sun set and the stars come out. It reminds me of stories by Mary O'Hara I had loved in my growing-up and young-adult years, especially *My Friend Flicka* and *Thunderhead*. Derek knows those books. They are set in Wyoming and the terrain where he grew up is very similar to the countryside she described.

When it gets cool and our tea is gone, we go in and play canasta, a game from my childhood, which Jim loves to play in its most virulent form, affectionately known as cut-throat canasta. I hadn't had much chance to play it when John was around, even in its non-cut-throat version. Family legend records what happened the first time I introduced the game to John. I recount the scene for Derek:

We were sitting at a card table in his parents' house. I was teaching John how to play canasta. It was my first visit to meet his parents, the Thanksgiving after we met. The afternoon was quiet with classical music playing in the background. Everyone else was off somewhere. After a few uneventful hands, the fateful hand was dealt. Soon John found himself in an impossible position. He couldn't take the pile because he didn't have two cards in his hand with which to do so. He couldn't go out because he didn't yet have a canasta. He couldn't play a card he drew on the cards he had already played because he had to discard, and still keep one card in his hand. He could continue to discard cards that I wanted and could take. Soon I had plenty of cards in order to keep him in this same pickle. It took him two or three plays to realize his dilemma fully.

When he did, he reacted with startling swiftness. He stood up and upended the table, cards and all, right into my lap, before I could even guess at his intention, much less get out of the way. I sat there open-mouthed, only realizing in retrospect that maybe I should have introduced the game to him a bit more gently. But even then, I didn't guess that would be the last time he would even consider playing canasta. Later he became quite a good bridge player, but the mere mention of canasta elicited from him a most uncharacteristic sneer, accompanied by muttered allusions to "melding, freezing the pile, and carrying on."

Derek is suitably impressed. Jim explains that one of the reasons this is a favorite family story is that it was so unusual for his father to take such violent and summary action. On the other hand, his stubbornness in refusing to ever play canasta again was highly characteristic.

Once we start playing, there seems to be no danger Derek will react as John did. For one thing, cut-throat, by its nature, precludes getting into that particular bind, as you draw two cards, rather than one. In addition, Derek, like Jim, seems to be able to remember every card in the discard pile, which grows and grows until one person can't resist taking it. That person then becomes a lone wolf playing against the other two, who become partners. When Jim is playing, I usually lose. He has already taught Derek to play two-handed canasta, but Derek hasn't played cut-throat before. Obviously, he's picked up the basic game and strategies well.

As I lean back on the bench beside the kitchen table, my feet up, I watch them. Jim has none of the forced animation I have sometimes seen in him. Instead, he seems perfectly relaxed. Occasionally his hand brushes against Derek's or their eyes meet in a shared thought. An unexpected burst of envy is my first, unexpected reaction, and I miss John's presence keenly.

Later, I find myself remembering Jim in years past. How he, at the age of two or three, would come into our bedroom early in the morning, long before we wanted to wake up. When I finally managed to open my eyes, his soft, dewy toddler skin, big blue eyes, blond curls and sturdiness would take my breath away. He was so beautiful, and I loved him so much. I remember him playing with the charcoal in the fire pit while his father and I struggled to get our old-fashioned tent up. That was when we went on a five-week camping trip when Jim was one year old. The blue suit that brought out the blue in his eyes was ruined, but we did get the tent up, and I learned not to bring clothes on camping trips unless I was willing to have them ruined.

Pictures taken of Jim and Tor, when they were about one and three, hung in the hall above the stairs in our big old house in Ann Arbor for years. Jim had his arm protectively around his younger brother, and the two of them looked into the camera with complete innocence and trust. Years later, I remembered the two of them walking ahead of the rest of a family group one Easter Sunday on the way home from church. Occasionally, we would catch fragments of their conversation: DOS, rams, roms. We knew none of us could participate in that computer-laden conversation, but we loved to see the two of them so obviously enjoying being together and sharing interests and information. Their friendship continued in high school. They were in theater together, and would often stay late working on sets with mutual friends. I also remember Tor saying, more recently, that Jim is the smartest person he has ever met.

Other images crowd into my mind: John and I driving him to Oberlin his freshman year, and how I cried almost the whole way back. Then there was the time he and John came back to camp dripping wet, having capsized our first, small sailboat. A gust of wind from Lake Michigan, funneled through openings in the sand dunes to Lake Hamlin, where they were sailing, caught them unprepared. Inexplicably, both of them seemed to be pleased with themselves. I never knew why, but suppose it was because the worst had happened and the only consequences were a few wet wallets and one lost cushion. I remember their preparations for, and glee upon completing, an overnight sailing trip to Put-in-Bay Island in Lake Erie a few years later.

On another note, I remember the argument the two of them had when Jim and Tor were both in college and John would not let Tor drive the motor home on a steep and winding path in Big Sur country in California. Jim, being more protective of his younger brother's honor than Tor was, stomped off to the back of the motor home. After a period of tense silence, John pulled over to a scenic overlook, stopped the vehicle and walked back to Jim. Grimly, he told him, "You are the stubbornest person I know—besides myself." The ensuing laughter broke the tension, and the two of them, so much alike in so many ways, dropped the argument without the need for any further words.

I remember the climbing tower John built for the kids when they were little and how they would sit up on top with their friends and neighbors, Meg and Kate, eating fresh raw peas from their garden. And how could I forget the day Jim fell out of a second-story window while watching a chipper in the neighbor's driveway grinding up limbs from a tree that had just been cut. At the hospital, he was cooperative and mostly silent, until we told him they might have to operate. I explained how the doctors thought he might be bleeding inside, so they would have to make a cut and find out where so they could sew it up. It wasn't until later that we realized we had forgotten to explain about anesthesia. No wonder he cried!

Fortunately, they never did have to operate, and Jim recovered with no scars except an inability to face a needle without becoming faint. I remember his disappointment when he tried to give blood as soon as he turned eighteen. He was fine until they poised the needle over his arm. Then he began to faint. The nurse caught him, revived him and gently explained that some people just *do* get faint and usually can't change that, no matter how much they want to be able to give blood. She quietly told him, "I think you are just going to have to find other ways to help humanity."

"Your turn, Mom." I look up at my adult son, at his extraordinary light blue eyes, at his features and facial expressions so like John's, and am struck again by how handsome he is and by how much I still love him, although in a very different way than when he was three. Then I look at my cards, at the spread of cards in front of Jim and Derek, at the discard pile, and draw two cards. Amazingly enough, they are two cards that let me go out and at least limit my losses. So I do. I still end the evening a substantial loser—at cards, anyway.

Chapter 16

The Trip to Pleasant Bay—Starting Out

The next day is a day of preparation. The mules are delivered around noon, and all three of us listen to the instructions for their care and feeding. Named Daisy and Pet, the mules seem quite amiable. We tether them, as instructed. During this process we keep Amber inside. Once the mules seem comfortable, we put Amber on a leash to introduce her. Her tail and ears are a study in suspicion and curiosity, but, after a few minutes, she seems to decide they are not a threat to her. The mules, for their part, are decidedly indifferent to her presence. When we let her off her leash, cautiously, she decides to ignore them, and turns her attention to our activities.

The mules' rental includes saddlebags, and we spread out our three compact tents, sleeping bags, cooking gear, lantern and food. Amber sniffs everything, but, surprisingly, leaves it all alone. As long as we put our clothes in day packs each of us will carry, we can get everything in the saddlebags, which are quite roomy. Keeping an eye on the animals, we review the menu I'd drawn up and check it against supplies and cooking gear. We try out the portable stove and the cook set and they work well enough to heat up some soup for lunch. We eat that, and some open-faced cheese sandwiches, and realize we are ready for the trip. With Amber, we walk up to Little Grassy, watch some whales, which are quite visible through my binoculars, and the gannets.

It is a warm afternoon, perfect for a swim in the cove. The water is, as usual, cold, but enjoyable after our exertions and I even manage to swim out to the rocks and back. After warming up in the sun and exploring the small beach, we climb back up the bluff and hill behind it to my cabin, shower, eat and play a game of scrabble, which I manage to win.

The next morning all three of us wake up early. It is cool and sunny, perfect hiking weather. The radio promises continued sunny, cool weather with intermittent cloudiness for the next, crucial days. After a hearty breakfast of eggs and pancakes, we load up the mules and start off. Amber, happy to be included, frolics all around us.

The decision is made to go by way of the lighthouse. It is right on the point between the Gulf of St. Lawrence and the St. Lawrence Bay, which leads out to the Atlantic Ocean. I haven't been there for a while, Jim and Derek haven't seen it, and it includes a nice stretch along the Gulf. Their owner has assured us that Daisy and Pet will not be bothered by the horses and cows usually seen on that trail.

The first part of the walk is along an old road and we all walk together. The boys bring me up to date on the latest zoo news. Derek has almost as much to offer as Jim. I assume they have gone there together on more than one occasion, as he seems to be well attuned to the Kingdon family zoo interests. The new Grasslands exhibit is open, and the bison look great amidst the towering prairie grasses; it is yet to be seen how long the grasses will last with the bison eating and trampling the same area every day. It looks as though there is some activity going on in the water birds area, but they can't puzzle out what the end result is supposed to be. With respect to the neighborhood, the lions on the Taft Street bridge still have not appeared, even though a new set just like the old was promised years ago.

Cutting off Old Fraser Road toward the lighthouse, we have to split up. Since Jim is the fastest walker, he takes the first turn with the mules.

I ask Derek about his mother.

"I guess Jim told you she died last winter," he began.

"Yes, Jim said she'd died recently, but he didn't tell me anything more about her."

Derek swallows hard and looks off to the Gulf. I touch his arm lightly, "I shouldn't have asked. I don't want to make things more difficult for you."

"No, it helps to talk about her. Besides, I want you to know, even though it is hard to talk about her death. She had a hard death—metastatic breast cancer. The family had known since her initial surgery five years ago that it might end the way it did. The good thing is that we all really treasured the time we had together. This is the first summer since her first surgery I haven't just hauled my books and research with me and spent the whole summer with her and Dad. I have two brothers, one older and one younger, and a sister, and they'd all come home as much as they could, too.

"The first few years were just plain fun. We'd go on trips—sometimes by horseback, sometimes by car and sometimes on foot. Mom had this great love of the Wyoming land, and instilled the same love in all of us. I remember once when we were driving along and saw the sun setting at the same time a thunderstorm was blowing up from the west. We stopped the car and got out so we could see the whole panorama and feel the wind of the approaching storm. When we got back in the car, she just said quietly, 'Well, that's worth being alive for.' Without any bitterness."

"Her death must have left a big hole," I say softly.

"Yes, it did. For me, especially for my father, of course, and my siblings. And for lots of other friends and relatives. She was always such a good listener, and so compassionate, wise and calm. Everyone loved being with her. Although her death was painful—the cancer spread to her bones—she loved having visitors right up to the last few weeks."

We both stop for a moment as we come to the top of a small rise and in sight of the Gulf again.

"Even though she was only fifty-four, she felt she had lived a full, satisfying life. She was at peace with everyone she knew, with herself and with God. Although I miss her terribly, I learned a lot about living—and about dying—from her."

"How was she about your being gay?" I ask after a moment of silence.

"Well, I told Mom first. It was after my junior year in college and I'd gone to PFLAG meetings, and talked with gay friends about how to tell my parents. I brought some pamphlets and books with me in case they would help them. You see, Mom was raised Mormon and she and Dad are both practicing Mormons. The Mormon church isn't very accepting of gays—although I know a lot of gay Mormons—so I knew it might be hard for them."

"Did your preparation help?"

"Well, yes and no. I think they did help my Mom, although she was pretty distraught. It probably didn't help that I was so nervous that I forgot what I'd planned to say and just blurted out, 'Mom, I'm gay.' " The last sentence is said with a rueful grin and a pause before he continues.

"She told me she loved me, and she didn't cry or tell me I was a sinner or anything, but I could tell she was in pain and really confused. She and Dad went away for the weekend later that day, and Dad tells me she burst into tears the minute they were out of sight of the house. He couldn't imagine what was wrong, and I guess it took her a full five minutes to even be able to talk about it.

"All I knew is that about ten minutes after they left, the phone rang, and it was Dad. I figured Mom would tell him, and was pretty nervous about how he'd react, but I didn't expect a reaction that fast!

"Nor did I expect him to react the way he did! It was a short conversation, and I can still remember every word of it: 'I love you. Mom tells me you're gay. I understand, and that's fine with me. We can talk more later when we get back, but I didn't want you to worry a minute more about my reaction.'

"Until I heard his words, I hadn't realized how worried I was about his reaction. I felt as though a burden had lifted from my shoulders. My Dad is a man of few words, strong morality, and he doesn't mince words. When we talked later, he told me that he'd gone to a diversity training program at work shortly after he began working for the local telephone company—which he started doing when I was in high school. That was about when he decided he'd rather be an avocational rancher than become part of big-scale ranching.

"Anyway, during the course of the training, he'd learned a lot about what it means to be gay or lesbian, and learned that one of his co-workers is gay. They became close friends, and he learned more from him about how cruel families and others can be, often out of ignorance and unthinking prejudice.

"I've been really lucky. Mom worked through her difficulties and my siblings, with Mom and Dad's help and example, have been great. I did drift away from most of the rest of Mom's family, who stick pretty closely to the Church's teaching that homosexuality is wrong. I've also drifted away from the Church. It's pretty hard to be a healthy, open gay in the Mormon Church today."

"Have you found another church home?" I ask.

"No. I guess I haven't really looked too hard. I'm still sorting out my beliefs, although I've never lost my faith in God or my sense of a close personal relationship with Him."

We walked along companionably for a while, each deep in our thoughts. I was thinking of how, at his age, I was less aware of God than he is.

"The last time I visited home before Mom died," Derek continued, "she told me of the message she felt had come from God not too long after I told her I was gay. It had healed her of all anguish and suffering over the issue of my sexual orientation. She had never forgotten the words, and they meant so much to me that I've memorized them, too:

> This is your child. This is who he is. Love him fiercely. Make sure he always knows that his homosexuality does not shut him off from God or moral goodness. Work to make sure there is always a place at the table for him. Make the world a better place for him and for others like him.

In her own way Mom did that until she became too sick. Even then, she made a point of speaking with pride about her gay son to those who took care of her or came to visit. And, because of who she was, many came. As a result, every once in a while, someone from home says something that shows the old ideas are beginning to change. It's sort of like water dripping on stone, though."

There's a bitterness in his tone that surprises me. "It must be hard, even though your family is so understanding."

"The funeral was hard—harder than it had to be. Certain so-called friends and relatives obviously assumed I was living some kind of wild, hedonistic, immoral lifestyle and would surely die of AIDS sooner or later. It didn't matter that they've known me all my life, and know that I'm just not that kind of person. For them it's as though being gay changes the way I am instead of being a part of who I am."

"There must be people like that in the Presbyterian Church, too," I acknowledge, "although if there are, I haven't met them, or they've kept their opinions to themselves. I did meet one Presbyterian father who is strongly against the ordination of gays, even though he has a gay son, with whom he says he's on good terms. I could never figure that out."

"Well, I must say I found the people at your church very welcoming."

"New York Avenue?" I am astonished; Jim did not usually show any more enthusiasm about going to church than his father had.

"Yeah," Derek grins at my reaction, apparently not surprised by it. "We went several times. Some people recognized Jim, and expressed their sympathy and asked after you. Others greeted us warmly, even though they didn't recognize him."

"I'm glad to hear that. Even though our church has studied the issues, and gone to bat for gays and lesbians on the local, regional and national level, we still do not usually have many gay male couples who attend services."

I'm also glad that Jim felt comfortable enough about my church to attend it without me, but I keep that to myself.

Jim joins us now for the last part of our conversation as we come out of the trees onto the grassy plateau leading up to the lighthouse. As I take the mules from him, I squeeze his hand and address him, "Hey, I'm glad you and Derek went to New York Avenue."

I'd never expected to see the day when he would again decide to attend church without any request from me. Although church had been important to him in his high-school years, it had often been a painful subject with him since then. In fact, it is the one subject we don't discuss freely, even now. Once I'd asked him if he'd be interested in what the young adults group was doing. He said there were several reasons he didn't want to attend, all related to the denomination's attitude toward gays and lesbians. I haven't pushed the subject, knowing that if and when he wants to talk about it, he'll let me know.

Of course, I would rather that both our sons were part of a welcoming, supportive church community. Then, too, I remember how far from church I was in my twenties and thirties. At that point, Mother's not-so-subtle pushes toward church only diminished any interest I might otherwise have had. I, too, like my sons, was raised in a home with a religious mother and a non-believing father. Both families believed that it is important for children to understand both perspectives and make their own decisions.

Most of the time, I feel fine about that. Sometimes, however, I get a lump in my throat when I realize that Jim's choice is so affected by realities beyond our control and Tor's is not. This is one of those times. Were things different in the Presbyterian denomination, our church might well have a group of single gays and lesbians that would provide a congenial church home and a compatible social group for Jim.

As usual, it is very windy at the point. We tether the mules in the lee of the lighthouse and find a place behind a hummock where we can enjoy the view while resting our feet and drinking our V-8 juice. From that spot we can't see anything but water beyond the cliff we are sitting on. Before moving on, we go over to the edge and admire the waves breaking upon the rocks beneath us. We look

around for the eagles that Ken said often hang around the point, but don't see any.

The path leads us southeast along the grassy bluffs above the Gulf. When we come to the steep ravine cut by some nameless river, which is now just a rivulet, we separate the mules. I hold Pet while Derek coaxes Daisy down the steep descent, across the water, and up the bank on the other side. Once Pet sees that Daisy could cross the divide, she willingly follows with just a little encouragement from me.

In the meantime, Jim has gone up to the mouth, finding the rockiest route, and is climbing over rocks and watching the spray sent up by the waves crashing against them. Amber has followed him, alternately watching him somewhat anxiously and clambering over the rocks herself with four-footed ease. She seems both intrigued and a bit intimidated by the waves. Walking toward them with tail held straight out behind her, she advances until a wave catches her, and then she quickly retreats, whimpering softly. She looks so funny with her bedraggled face and dripping fur and her tail in kind of a question mark that we can't help but laugh at her.

Watching Jim, I remember past rock-climbing exploits. When he was two, I first discovered what appeared to be an in-born love of rock climbing. We were spending a year in Washington while John did some research. We had become close friends with a woman and her daughter, Lisa, who lived just down the hall from us in the apartment we were renting. Jim was normally much less adventurous than Lisa. At four months older than Jim, Lisa led most of their play. The day we went out to the Great Falls of the Potomac River, however, Jim surprised us all by leaving Lisa, and indeed both of us moms, far behind as he scrambled over the rocks away from the riverbank.

The year we were in California, almost twenty years later, just after Jim had told us, yes, he really was gay, it was not just a passing fad, the four of us went camping in the Anza-Borrego Desert east of San Diego. While we were hiking along a stream in the bottom of a canyon, all of a sudden Jim was climbing up the side. Tor followed him for a ways, and then gave up. On the way back, Jim still was not down, and we sat and waited for him as we watched a storm boiling up out of what had been a completely blue, calm sky. Fortunately, he saw it too and got back in time for all of us to make it to the car before the deluge hit.

Now I wonder if that desert climb had the same origin as the scare we had just after Tor was born. When he was all of two days old or so, I took Jim out for a walk, his first outing since Tor's birth. Suddenly Jim startled me by uncharacteristically darting out into Connecticut Avenue, a major six-lane thoroughfare. Luckily, it was early on a Sunday morning, and there was hardly any traffic, so I was able to rescue him without mishap. Afterward I wondered if Jim, unable to articulate his complex feelings in a new and probably threatening situation, was acting out a question: Did we still love him enough to run after him, or had he been displaced by this new creature? Was his climb up that canyon wall a way of wordlessly asking us if we still loved him enough to try to follow him on a route none of us had any experience with?

We'd tried, in our own slow ways. And today I can watch him serene in the knowledge that he is not trying to run away from me, but is just following his natural bent. We had, in fact, supported him fully as we had followed him into new territory, at least after our initial shock, even though, like Amber, we had sometimes been surprised and befuddled by the journey.

This time, Jim neither scares us nor keeps us waiting. By the time I get Pet across, he is there to praise the mules for their sure-footed passage of a tricky spot in the trail. Shortly after that, we begin seeing horses. We put Amber on a leash, as we have no desire to see what she might do with or to them if she were left free. The mules and the horses notice each other, but, with nostrils flaring slightly, and ears at the alert, decide to ignore each other. As we approach Lowland Cove, we begin seeing cattle and give them a wide berth. My previous experience suggests that these cattle are more territorial and less placid than the gentle Holsteins I knew as a child. Neither Amber nor the mules object to being held tightly until we are well past them.

When the path veers off into the woods, Derek goes ahead with the mules and Jim and I follow. We've let Amber off the leash again, and she runs freely back and forth, making sure that we are all still under her care and protection.

"Well, what do you think?" he asks.

"I like him. I like the way you are with each other. You seem to be very comfortable with him, and he with you. He is smart, has a good sense of humor and seems to appreciate your sense of humor, and yet he is serious and interesting to talk to. And he likes animals."

"What do you think Dad would think?"

"Hmmm. Hard question. I know he would like the fact that he's a professor—even if it is in history!" John's professed disdain for history, despite, or maybe even because of, his brother's renown in the field, had been a source of amusement within the family. "He would enjoy his wit. I don't know if you really knew how much he enjoyed your wit and how often he would recount examples of that."

"I guess I'm not surprised to hear that. We'll miss that, won't we?" We are both quiet, each with our own memories. I am remembering John and the "kids," raucously recounting stories which were funnier in the retelling than in the experiencing. It seemed only yesterday, for instance, that Jim had us all laughing until tears rolled down our faces. He'd told us of the care with which he had packed a lunch using up all the perishables in his refrigerator before he departed for a business trip out West last fall. And his disappointment when he realized, on the plane after a hurried departure, that it was his lunch he'd thrown down the trash chute, instead of the garbage. I find myself reaching for my handkerchief.

"I wish Dad could be here." Jim voices the thought I'm not sure I can say without bursting into tears. Instead of answering, I reach for him and sob on his shoulder. He hugs me back and, in tears himself, says, "Somehow, I thought he would always be here." Amber, ever sensitive to mood, brings us back to the present by circling around us and whimpering.

After I regain my composure, I realize and voice the limits of my ability to guide Jim. "Jim, I just want you to have a relationship like your father and I had. I know that's what he wanted for you, too. That takes commitment and a willingness to work through the difficult issues that arise in any relationship. And I think it also requires compatibility, attraction and a good choice in a mate. One of the things that your father did while he was deciding whether or not to ask me to marry him was something I did not like at the time, but that now seems very wise to me. He talked to a minister he trusted about whether or not he should go forward. I think it is important that you identify and talk about any reservations you have about going forward with the relationship with someone you trust, me or Tor or Greta or some other relative or friend.

"I really like what I've seen of Derek so far, but I don't know whether you and he can, or even want to, develop the kind of secure relationship John and I had. I'm willing to do anything I can to help you decide, though."

"Well, my heart tells me to go ahead."

"That's a good sign—probably a necessary first ingredient for a good relationship. What about your head?"

"I think the thing I wonder about the most is whether we'll be able to develop the kind of relationship you and Dad had. I feel that we have some elements of it, but, of course, we aren't where you were, not yet."

"Well, you should remember that it took a lot of time, a lot of hard work and a certain amount of pain to develop our relationship. If we'd waited to get married until we had that kind of relationship, it never would have happened." I pause for a moment, trying to sort out the key ingredients. "I think the most important element, after love, was trust. We knew that each of us wanted the best for the other and would never knowingly or deliberately hurt the other. That meant we could be completely honest with each other—probably most importantly when we felt 'lower than whale shit,' as we used to put it. I guess one important question at this point is whether you can share your self-doubts and low moments with each other."

Jim is silent for a while. "That's a good question. You know that it's not easy for me to share my emotions with anyone."

"I know. And it's possible that you don't need the same kind of encouragement I did. Without John's support, comfort and pride in me, I'm not sure I would have even tried to do some of the things that were most rewarding to me. Remember how he used to call me the 'Grand Fromage' when I became the executive director of the physician's group?"

"Yes, I do. I remember how I thought it was funny, but also how it made me feel good inside. I guess I kind of took Dad's pride in you for granted." Jim is smiling as he remembers. "But, looking back, and based on different couples I have seen, I can see how some husbands might have been threatened by their wife's success."

"Well, even more than a 'booster' like that, I think everyone needs someone to lend a sympathetic ear and honest, caring reactions when it feels like the world is caving in on them, and they're feeling inadequate to deal with whatever is facing them. I know your father needed that when he was chair of the department or at a hard place in his research or writing."

"That makes a lot of sense, Mom. Thanks." Jim gives me a quick hug and goes bounding up to Derek to point out a meadow where we can eat our lunch.

For the first time in a long time I am overcome with a sense of awe and gratitude to God for his love and support, as well as His exquisite sense of timing. Difficult as it is to advise Jim without John's input and insights, trying to help him think through his relationship with Derek helps me appreciate in a new way what a gift my relationship with John was. And, strangely enough, in doing so, I feel less alone than I have since the day John died.

Chapter 17

Pollett Cove

Most of our walk that afternoon is through thick woods. The path is good and well marked, but sometimes so narrow we have to walk single file. I usually lead the way, with Amber making sure we do not surprise any wildlife. Even with that, we do catch glimpses of several deer bounding through the forest in flight from the dreaded dog. But no bears are in evidence, although we do see bear droppings periodically, which Amber sniffs carefully out of curiosity and, her body language makes clear, a sense of duty.

The terrain that looked like gentle, rolling undulations from Bear Cove Mountain is steeper on the ground. Our views are of trees, either up close or off in the distance. There are lovely sugar maples and what my guidebook says are yellow birch trees, and we comment on how lovely it must be in autumn. At one point the trail leads us up a small mountain. A break in the woods at the top gives us a view of hills and valleys, all wooded, but no water, even though we know we are not very far from the coast. After that our trail, which has been gradually ascending and leading fairly straight south, takes a jog to the southeast before turning due west and then southwest. We are now gradually descending. It is cool in the woods and shady, although we can see the sun glinting on the leaves.

Suddenly, after a steep descent, we are on a bare bluff overlooking Pollett Cove. Why hasn't anyone told us it is so beautiful? The late afternoon sun sparkles on the blue waters and illuminates a curved, sandy bay, divided by the small, but noisy, Blair River. Around the edges is a sandy verge with a few scattered boulders. The strip of sand is wide to the south where the land gently rises to a wooded rim. To the north, a sliver of sand narrows to nothing as it abuts a steep cliff which borders the cove off to our right.

By the time we make our way down, the sun is low in the sky over the water. We take the saddlebags off the mules, water them, and tether them in a nice grassy spot well away from our campsite, unload the bags, set up our tents, fix an unambitious cold supper and build a small fire with dry wood close to the campsite. I, however, do not last long, and crawl into my warm sleeping bag, taking Amber with me into the tent where she curls up at my feet. Both of us soon fall into a sound sleep.

I wake up early the next morning, glad for my cozy sleeping bag and the warmth of Amber who is, by now, sprawled across the bottom of my bag, still sound asleep. For a mostly indoor dog, yesterday was quite a workout. The sun is not yet up over the hills in back of us, and the air is distinctly chilly. The view out my tent's front door is pretty, but subdued in the early morning light. Not enough to stir me into action. My new tent is small, and the logistical challenge of getting dressed is more than I care to undertake at the moment.

When I wake up again, the sun is sparkling on the water. Derek is engaged in what looks like promising breakfast-making maneuvers. Jim is dipping water from the river. The combined stimuli of the sun, hunger, a long night's sleep and Amber's cold wet nose get me moving. I let Amber out to take care of her morning duties, after which she ambles over to investigate what Jim and Derek are doing. It doesn't take me long to get dressed, even in my cramped quarters.

By the time I get out to the campsite, the water is well boiled and being distributed between our hot cocoa mugs and pancake mix. Jim and I sip our cocoa while Derek starts flipping pancakes. We help him hold the skillet on the slippery, and not altogether level, surface of the propane one-burner "stove." It doesn't take us long to decide unanimously to stay another night in this charmed spot. Besides, the hike yesterday was longer and more strenuous than I'd done for a long time and my muscles join in voting for a lazy day enjoying the scenery and the company.

Cleaning up doesn't take long and then Jim and Derek change into swimming suits for a dip in the relatively warm waters of the

Gulf. It is too cool, and I'm too lazy to join them. After brushing my teeth and taking my vitamins, I take a book and a freshly made cup of herbal tea to a sunny spot next to a big boulder, which serves as a convenient backrest. The guys are frolicking about in the shallow water, splashing each other and laughing. The sun sparkles on the water, lighting it up like iridescent jewelry as the spray is caught by the light. I watch the two of them, Jim with his dark-brown hair, handsome, trim and graceful, and Derek, a little taller and a little stockier, just as handsome, with his red hair lit up by the sun. Amber, of course, is right in there with them, and her wet fur looks almost like taffy held up to the light. Quite a trio!

A wave of peaceful contentment washes over me, followed by a slight shock of surprised recognition, and then a surge of gratitude. I had thought I would never feel that familiar wave again. I had thought that, like Gretchen in Goethe's *Faust*, "meine Ruh ist hin." That is one of the few phrases I remember from my college German. I had thought my peace was gone, at least for the duration of my days on earth.

After their swim, Jim and Derek check on the mules, who are happily grazing, and decide to go exploring. I have no desire to move and, in fact, haven't even felt ambitious enough to begin reading.

Eventually, I do pick up my book and become absorbed in its story of the Lewis and Clark expedition through the uncharted wilderness that became United States territory with the Louisiana Purchase. The book was one of John's last gifts to me, and I'm sorry we didn't have an opportunity to discuss it. Still, I feel close to him while reading it, and reexperience the warm glow of appreciation I felt when he gave me a gift so well designed to appeal to my love of adventure, history, nature, exploring and good writing. Our journey is incredibly civilized compared with theirs. In some ways we have the best of civilization and of wilderness. Even though the area we are hiking was logged, the second growth is now large enough to hide that fact from the casual observers we are. And, not only do we not meet hostile Indians, as Lewis and Clark did, we have not met anyone or even seen any signs of man's presence, other than the trail we are walking on, since we turned inland and left the cows and horses grazing behind us.

By the time the explorers return, bursting with energy and high spirits, I'm ready to join them for a swim. Several swims, in fact. Each time I return to the water it seems a little warmer. My last swim is one of my "epic" swims: long and leisurely with good views along the coast. North of the cove, the cliff is steep and continues as far as I can see. No wonder the path doesn't follow the coast there! The coast to the south is gentler, and I hope our path will be close enough to the shore to be able to see the changing coastline. As I return to the beach, Amber swims out to meet me, as though to make sure that I'm all right. I am strangely touched and reflect that dogs sure are different from the cats who were our pets for so many years!

Over dinner, as we watch the sun setting over the water, Jim, with an air of suppressed expectancy, blurts out, "Mom, Derek and I have an announcement." At this, Derek and he simultaneously jump to their feet, put their arms around each other, and, looking into each other's eyes, break out in song, "Do you love me as I love you? Will you be as true as true? Will you promise with me to stay?" The tune is exuberant and vaguely familiar, and the whole performance has such an air of comedic excess, that I burst out laughing—as do both of them.

"So, I take it," I say when I regain my ability to speak, "that this is a happy announcement?"

"Yes, it is. We've decided to have a commitment ceremony, although we aren't ready to make a public announcement."

"You mean this isn't public?" I ask, still giggling, and waving an arm to include us, Amber, the mules and the magnificent scenery.

"Well, I guess it is in a way," responds Derek, with a grin. "And we don't mean we're going to keep it a secret. We just want to live with the possibility a while before we set the date, start making formal plans and telling everyone."

"And," Jim chimes in, "Derek needs to meet Tor and I want to meet his family."

"When will all that happen?" I ask.

"Well, Tor is talking about coming for one of his September visits." Jim looks at Derek.

"And my family is visiting at Thanksgiving," adds Derek.

"Have you thought about when you might have this ceremony?"

"Maybe around Christmas. That way it can't get too elaborate." Greta planned her wedding for two weeks after she and her fiancé decided to get married for just that reason. It had been a lovely, simple family ceremony with a maximum amount of time for enjoying the occasion and each other and a minimum of fuss. Jim is, in many ways, much like his aunt Greta.

"How about where?" I look at both of them, but Derek answers first.

"Good question. We've just been talking about that. That's probably one of the reasons we went to your church. If we do have it in church, that's the most likely candidate."

"You know I would love that!"

"Yes, Jim thought that you might. The other possibilities are either a home or some public spot."

"Have you thought about where you will live?" Without answering, Derek looks at Jim.

"Well, we've talked about it, but haven't made any decisions. Not my apartment. Derek has a house in American University Park, which is nice. I just have to decide if I am ready to share home-owning. He is close to the Tenleytown Metro, so I wouldn't have to get a car." Jim's distaste for travel by car is well known in our family. He is a good driver, and will drive if necessary, but much prefers public transportation, foot or bike.

"Derek, I haven't even asked you about where you live!" I surprise myself, since one of my hobbies is exploring various D.C. neighborhoods. How could I have failed to ask Derek about that subject?

"Well, it's a well-built house about 70 years old on a quiet, tree-shaded street. It's about a twenty-minute walk to work. I have a private backyard and space for a vegetable garden, although I'm growing flowers for cutting this year. Good neighbors and room for my dog and cats."

Startled, I turn to Jim with raised eyebrows and reproachful face: "You didn't tell me he had pets!" Such an oversight could not have been accidental. I still miss our three cats, who died at the ripe old ages of seventeen, eighteen and twenty-three years, but haven't been ready to take on another twenty-year commitment. He knows how much I would love to have cats in the family.

"Yeah, I thought I'd let you get to love him for himself, and not for his cats!"

"Very smart. So, if you move there, Jim, what would you do with the business?" Jim's bedroom now doubles as his office and the living room as his employees' office.

"Well, I've been looking at office space for a couple of months now. Of course, if I move out, we'd have more space in the apartment and might be able to continue to use it as our office." I remember that one of his former employers operated out of several apartments when Jim first started working with them.

"Pretty exciting stuff." That is an understatement as thoughts and possibilities swirl around in my head. But I know I need to give them time and space to explore their options, including time to face any doubts they have about making a commitment to each other. I know Jim well enough to know that when he does make such a commitment it will not be made lightly. Derek seems like the kind of person for whom that is true also, but time and further discussion will reveal whether it is or not. I feel a little bit like the stereotypical old-fashioned father who wants to ask his daughter's beau whether his intentions are honorable. But I don't think a direct question would be very illuminating.

Besides, for better or worse, those ways are behind us. I will do whatever I can to help Jim make the decision, but, ultimately, it is his. I remember our first premonitions about Tor's soon-to-be wife and asking Tor later, after the divorce, if it would have helped if we had spoken up then even more forcefully than we had, or had refused to participate in the wedding, or something dramatic like that. His answer confirmed our gut feelings at the time: "No, it just would have driven a wedge between me and my family. I was too much in love at the time to be willing to walk away from the marriage; I knew there might be problems, but I thought we'd work them out."

We are all quiet for a few minutes, savoring a certain solemnity about the occasion. I know that whatever happens with Derek and Jim, I'm grateful to have been included in these early discussions, and to have shared in this trip. I've gotten to know Derek, both as a person and as a future son-in-law, and to help Jim clarify his feelings and his thinking about commitment before they'd made a decision. I hope my discussion with Jim helped the two of them; I know it has helped me. For the first time since John's death, I deeply care and am involved in something which is all about the future, not the past, or how I am going to get through my present pain. That just plain feels good.

And I am excited and pleased about their decision. I smile at the two of them. Derek and Jim obviously agree with me that this is pretty exciting stuff. In unison they look into each other's eyes, reach for each other's hands, nod solemnly and then break into grins. With their grins, the mood changes again to one of celebration. Amber senses the change in mood and comes romping over from where she was lying, head between her paws, watching us as we talked. By now it is completely dark, so we gather up the dead, dry wood and kindling twigs Jim and Derek collected on their walk. While they are getting a fire started in the fire ring thoughtfully provided, I fish out a bottle of good wine I'd stuck into a crevice in Pet's saddlebags at the last moment, and three paper cups. We sit on the ground around the modest but warm fire, sip our wine and sing songs until the wine and firewood are both gone, and we can't remember any more songs.

As the last embers die down, we look up and are so astonished by the brightness of the stars that we all grab our sweatshirts, go down to the beach, lie on our backs and talk about stars and spacecraft. I'm the first to admit I'm getting sleepy (especially since talk of spacecraft does not have to get very deep before I am lost) and to heave my weary but happy body from the beach and into my bed. Amber follows without the need for an invitation.

As I lie in my warm sleeping bag with Amber's soft warm weight pressing against my legs, I send prayers of gratitude to God and reflect on the phrase, "life goes on," with new appreciation. I'm profoundly sorry that John is not here to share this joy with me. And I miss him next to me. Amber is a welcome presence, but hardly a substitute for him. At the same time, I'm also profoundly grateful that I am able to feel joy again.

With a bit of a start, I realize that from the moment of John's death until now, I had, without consciously knowing it, assumed that all my happy moments were behind me. If life is a river, I had been in a stagnant, unmoving pool, and now I was being caught up by the current. With God's help, Jim and Derek have given me, in a different way, the gift I gave Jim years ago—the gift of life.

Chapter 18

Heading Home

The next morning is cloudy, which makes it easier to move on. We all feel some reluctance to leave a spot whose physical loveliness has been an integral part of what we all know we will look back on for years to come as a wonderful, magical time. Magical in the sense that I anticipate being able to hold the memory in my hand, as I would a particularly lovely painted Christmas ornament, as a symbol of a special moment among the three of us and between us and God. Our spirits have all been touched and changed by the experience. We will never be exactly as we were when we arrived in Pollett Cove.

It is later than we expect it to be before we set out. Fixing and cleaning up after breakfast, taking down our tents, getting the mules ready, packing lunch and then the saddlebags—all is done in silence, almost meditatively. Even Amber is subdued. The mood is only intensified when, just as we set out, we spot a bald eagle on the cliffs above us. He watches us and we watch him until he lightly jumps into the air, majestically spreads his wings and sails over our heads. We are silent until he disappears behind the woods to the north, then smile at each other and set off on the trail south to Pleasant Bay, Amber running ahead and barking to warn off any ferocious attackers.

This section of the trail does go along the coast, as I had hoped. The solid cloud cover is breaking up. The wind whips the clouds into different shapes, some white and fluffy and some dark and threatening with their own internal source of movement and change. Intermittently the sun breaks through and dances on the waves. Watching the clouds as they ceaselessly reconfigure themselves is fun in and of itself. The dramatic setting with the constantly changing coastline only enhances our pleasure.

It is my turn with the mules. Jim, Derek and Amber are far ahead of me. I know they will wait for me at a suitable tree or rock on which to sit, if there is a particularly good view or if the trail becomes tricky to follow.

I'm happy to be left with my thoughts. I feel like a kaleidoscope myself. One moment I'm elated and the next on the verge of tears. Of course, weddings often make me cry, so I might feel that way even if it weren't for the poignancy of John's absence at this crucial time. Then I find myself thinking of practical questions: Will Jim and Derek want a minister to officiate at their service? If so, who? One of my ministers? My friend, Annabelle, who is by now, if all has gone according to plan, an ordained minister herself and installed in a position as a chaplain? And how will they want to refer to each other after the ceremony? Spouse? Husband? Partner? Lover? I've heard all of these used by gay and lesbian couples. I like the first three myself, but not "lover." Just why I feel that way is not clear. Maybe because it doesn't imply anything about commitment and the others do. How many people will they want to invite? If they don't have the ceremony in church, what are some good public places for the ceremony—in December? And what will Stephanie and Sonia think?

It is a good thing I'm walking alone. As usual, in my enthusiasm, I'm rushing things. First they need, as they have wisely pointed out, to live with the idea of a commitment to each other for a while. First they have to meet more of each other's family. First they have to make sure they are ready to make a long-term (hopefully lifetime) commitment, individually and as a couple. First they have to give any doubts either of them have time to surface and be explored. It is nice they had a good friendship before they began to think of each other in romantic terms. But, now that they have fallen in love, they have to make sure more than chemistry is bringing them together.

With all my thoughts, it seems like no time until I come upon the three of them sprawled on a rocky outcropping overlooking the gulf. The sun is out, the rock is warm and it is a perfect spot for lunch. We tether the mules, dig out our lunches and eat them in as lovely a place as we could have asked for. Jim and I find ourselves telling Derek about the trip the four of us took last summer to West Virginia to celebrate Jim's 30th birthday. The rock we are on is somewhat reminiscent of the limestone outcroppings on the trail we hiked, although the view there was of rolling mountains and peaceful valleys with farms and houses scattered along the river valley.

This leads to memories of John. I tell Jim that John told me, not too long before he died, he thought Jim and Tor had introduced the phrase "belts and suspenders" into the family. Certainly I knew the phrase as an apt description of their father's habit of checking everything at least twice.

"I don't remember who first used the phrase," Jim responds. "But I do remember how well it described him. Remember when we were in Norway, taking the train up to Trondheim, and he had three timetables? Every time we arrived in a station, he would check all three schedules, and fret about any discrepancies. I guess the fact that we had to change trains was what made him so compulsive, but I was just embarrassed at first. Then I began to see the humor in it."

"It was pretty funny. And it did have the advantage of meaning none of us had to worry at all about the logistics!"

"And remember how he used to tie knots on the sailboat? He used bowline knots most places." In an aside to Derek, Jim explained: "Bowline knots are foolproof—the strongest knots there are. But that wasn't enough for Dad. He tied 'enhanced' bowline knots with a couple of extra twists just to make sure they would never let go!"

I'm chuckling as I remember more of John's ways. "Remember how he would, after he locked the garage door, put a nail in the side of the lock, just to make sure that, even if someone unlocked the door with a key, they couldn't get in?"

"I sure do! How could I forget those times when I would try to come in that way with my key, and couldn't get in because of the nail. But the example I remember best was the time I was visiting in D.C. while I still lived in Minneapolis. The day before my return, Dad asked me if I had reconfirmed my return plane flight. I assured him I had, even though he is the only person I know who reconfirms flights these days. He left the room, and came back about five minutes later, cheerfully reporting, 'yup, your plane flight is all confirmed.' He'd obviously called the airline just to make sure that I *had* reconfirmed." Jim laughs as he remembers this. Then he stops.

"It used to really make me angry when he did that. I think at one point in my life, I felt he was checking everything I'd done because he did not trust me and that used to infuriate me. Then, as I grew up, I realized this did not have anything to do with me, my competence or his respect for my competence. It was just a habit of his. He probably learned it from his father." John's father had died three years to the day before my father did. Jim had been thirteen years old. Old enough to remember his grandfather's sometimes exasperating ways. "Or his mother. I remember the time Dad and I were building the bunkhouse in Cable and she kept making suggestions." Jim turns to Derek and explains, "Cable is our family vacation spot in northern Wisconsin that I told you about." Derek nods.

"I think you're right. And don't forget that his mother was also a champion worrier. Given that background, he did pretty well!"

"Guess that's right. Anyway, even though I don't remember him coming right out and saying so, I know he did respect my competency. I remember how he thanked me for reading and commenting on his last book and then thanked me again after he had read my comments and talked to me about a few of them."

"Yes, he had a deep appreciation of you, as well as of your intellect, your integrity, your instincts and your broad stock of interests and useful knowledge. That was, of course, on top of an abiding love for you, even when the two of you were being stubborn with each other. Remember the time you refused a ride into town from the cabin in Cable? You were going to catch a bus and a thunderstorm was coming. He was determined not to let you come to any harm, even though you told him you did not want or need a ride."

"And I was just as determined not to accept a ride, even if it did mean I would get soaked."

"I don't think he was worried about your getting soaked, but about the lightning."

"And I was at the stage where that worry infuriated me. I don't really know why, looking back, I was so angry about it, or so determined to walk."

"Well, in the end, I guess he was more determined than you were."

"Well, yes. Plus, he had the reality of the weather on his side. As the storm got closer and closer, the idea of getting soaked just to make some kind of point seemed less and less appealing."

"That may have been one of your last confrontations, wasn't it?"

"I guess so. I don't really remember exactly when it was. It's actually the only confrontation I remember since I graduated from college. Of course, there were other times when I would get my back up over something he said. But not very often, especially in the last few years." We are all silent with our own thoughts for a few minutes, until Jim resumes, "I trust Dad knew how much I loved him. I'm not sure I ever told him."

"Nor he you—at least, not often. But I have absolutely no doubt that he died loving you and knowing you loved him." That brings tears to his eyes and I, moved by a manifestation of emotion I hadn't seen in him since he was a kid, reach over and give him a hug. He returns it, reaches to include Derek, whose eyes are also wet, and the three of us hug each other a few moments with tears on our cheeks. Amber breaks the mood by trying to climb in among us and lick away our tears, whimpering in empathy. Of course, this makes us laugh and, with that, we all push off for the final stretch of our journey.

*

* *

It is almost shocking to look down on the little settlement of Red River just north of Pleasant Bay and see houses. The sandy beach looks inviting, though, and we are ready for a final swim in the warm waters of the Gulf. By the time we finish swimming and duck back into the shelter of the woods to change, the sun is low enough in the sky so that we know it is time to stop dawdling and get the mules home. Daisy and Pet, sensing they are on the home-stretch, are happy with the faster pace.

The sun is low by the time we have returned the mules to their owner and unloaded the saddlebags into the rental car. Derek offers to treat us to dinner at the Rusty Anchor, and we happily accept. Although Amber's nose is out of joint as she has to wait in the car, we promise her a treat and leave with no guilty feelings, despite her pitiful face. We sit by the window and watch in silence as the setting sun lights up the lingering clouds. I'm much too contented and absorbed in the changing scene before us to need to break the silence.

As we drive the rental car back to Bear Cove along the familiar route, we see the full moon rising over the mountains in front of us, chased and partially obscured at times by the remaining wisp of clouds. What a way to end the trip!

Chapter 19

Trip to Ingonish

It is a pleasure cooking breakfast in a kitchen that seems spacious and well appointed after our trail cooking facilities. The scrambled eggs with cottage cheese and fresh chives from the plant growing outside the back door remind Jim and me of John, the family "eggspert." His reputation started the year I went to work when he was on sabbatical. He took the morning shift and took turns with the neighbors fixing lunches, and I was home early for the late afternoon and fixing dinner stint. John had never expanded his repertoire much beyond eggs, but he had fixed wonderful scrambled eggs with cottage cheese. Even though I'm not the eggspert, mine taste pretty good. Toast and freshly made frozen orange juice complete our repast.

After breakfast, Jim and Derek take over in the kitchen and I walk down to the campground office to pick up my mail. While I'm there, I pet the cats and tell Sadie how much we admire the handiwork of Ken and his fellow employees during the three years he worked for the provincial Department of Natural Resources building the trail and how well maintained it is. She says it's good to see Amber frolicking around, but not bothering the campers. I notice that Amber is sticking pretty close to me. Sadie is glad to hear how much all of us, including Amber, enjoyed the hike.

The mail includes promising packets from Sonia and Stephanie, a package from Greta and what looks like a card from Tor. With a start, I remember it is my birthday. I knew that, of course, but forgot it in the excitement of the last few days. I drag a lawn chair from the porch to the front yard so I can enjoy the sun's warmth while I read. Sonia has sent an especially nice card of appreciation and good wishes. As usual, I feel a rush of gratitude for having the sisters I do and for the relationships we have with each other. Each of her kids has sent me a special card of their own design. Michael's, as usual, is very witty. Peter's is a splendid study in colors—all, I assume, from the treasured set of magic markers I sent him a year ago. Sofia, Elisa and Matthew all include references to their never-to-be-forgotten trip to Washington a year and a half earlier. Elisa's card includes a poignant reference to John. The two of them had had a special bond for years.

The greetings from Stephanie and her family are just as heart-warming. Stephanie's note speaks of how close she's come to feel to me and my family in the space of a few short years and of how being included in sad occasions as well as happy has deepened these feelings of closeness. She has been praying for me during this difficult time of grief and adjustment and hopes that I feel God's love and support, as well as the knowledge that I'm loved by her whole family. The kids' notes, like those from Sonia's family, include references to good memories they have from our last visit, and hopes to see me soon. Chris includes information he learned for his latest animal project about the reintroduction of wolves into the Olympic Peninsula, as well as memories of his visit to D.C. a year ago.

The package from Greta contains another wonderful note and a beautiful, all-cotton summer nightgown. I reflect wryly that she must have noticed my collection of threadbare and make-do summer nightgowns when she visited. Once again she has come up with a perfect gift.

The card from Tor has a picture of a cat on the front. Not only does the cat look exactly like Tor's childhood pet, Charley, he also is sitting in Charley's classic "Egyptian cat" pose on an old-fashioned newel post with his tail hanging down. The printed greeting, "Happy birthday to a real cool cat," is augmented by a simple note in Tor's handwriting, "Much as I miss Dad, I still feel lucky in the 'parent dept.' " He also includes a letter with the news that he's planning to visit D.C. in less than a month. He wonders if he can stay with me, rather than Jim, as he usually does, in light of the increased activity at Jim's office/apartment.

Tor also says that he has been thinking about the boat. He knows, of course, that it is in the water and that we'd been on our way to go sailing when John had his fatal stroke. It will be very difficult, he writes, to go out on the boat again. It was so much his father's boat. Still, he thinks we should put it up for the winter as we always have. We can decide later what to do with it. Anyway, in addition to meeting Derek, one of the purposes of his trip will be to help me get the boat over to its winter home. Maybe we can even go for a sail if the weather is nice.

Until I notice how relieved I feel at the prospect of his help with the boat, I hadn't realized how much I'd been dreading dealing with that particular loose end. Going out to John's cherished boat alone would be more of an ordeal than I feel ready to contemplate. And, having never captained the boat, I'm not sure I remember everything I need to know to get it over to Shadyside. But, with Tor's capable help, I'm sure we can figure out everything we will need to know.

I put down his card and think how characteristic it is for him to be so considerate and thoughtful. And I know that it won't be any easier for him than it will be for me to sail on the craft that is so imbued with memories of John. I remember some of the happy times we had with Tor on the boat. Even though he lived across the country, it seemed as though he always brought good weather with him when he came. Some of our best sailing days were with him. Only when Tor was at the helm, did I ever see John lie on the deck and look contentedly up into the rigging as we sailed along. Jim was perfectly capable of taking the helm, as was I, but neither of us enjoyed it the way Tor did.

The first time Tor came to visit us after John bought the boat—aptly named "Academic Freedom"—each day he and John would go through a ritual. "Well, what should we do today?" John would ask. "We could go to a museum," he would continue, naming a couple of possibilities. "Well," Tor would reply thoughtfully, "what's the weather like?" "Or," his father would reply, answering his question by implication "we could go sailing." Each day we went sailing, and each day we had wonderful weather and memorable sailing. The last day of that visit, we lingered out on the water, all of us hating to go in. By the time we came to the river leading to our marina, dusk was falling. In the shadows on the woodsy, undeveloped riverbank on our left, we saw shapes, and realized with wonder that they were great blue herons, settling in to sleep for the night.

No, it wouldn't be easy for Tor to get on that boat again, knowing that never again would John stand at the helm. But how like him to think of how hard it would be for me, to know that he could help, and to courageously offer to do so. Much as I miss John, I am blessed to have the wonderful children I do.

Sitting in the sun with Jim and Derek's voices in the background and surrounded by good wishes from my family, I feel very close to God. My eyes travel to the ocean, to the cliffs and the hills behind me. I marvel at the ability to feel contented again, even though the ache in my heart is still there.

By the time I'm ready to move to the porch, Jim and Derek are finished with the dishes and are consulting maps and tour guides. "How about going over to St. Lawrence Bay and going whale watching on Ken's boat?" Jim suggests. He and Derek have seen the signs for Ken's whale-watching rides, and heard the story of how Ken transforms his fishing boat into a passenger vehicle, after the end of each fishing season, with a thorough scrubbing and a fresh coat of paint.

"Sounds good to me." I haven't been on a tour yet this summer, and it would be fun to see the lighthouse we'd seen by land from the different perspective of a boat.

We arrive at the turnoff for the fishing village of Bay St. Lawrence with time to spare. So, we continue up the road to its end at a bluff overlooking the village and the St. Lawrence Bay into which the protected little harbor leads. We park the car in the parking lot that both marks the end of the road and the start of a trail which leads eventually to the Money Point Light. We take the lunch we have packed over to a conveniently placed picnic table and eat it looking down at the fishing boats and the birds circling them. It is strange to be eating without Amber waiting hopefully for dropped food, but she seemed contented enough to be left behind in the by-now-familiar cabin. We didn't think her presence in the boat would encourage seeing wildlife.

Pretty soon we spot Ken's boat chugging around Black Point and, eventually, into the harbor. That is our signal to pack up and drive back down to get our tickets. We greet Ken and he suggests we get our fish for dinner before we start on the tour or we'll miss the fishermen. Once we have done that, he puts our package on the ice he keeps in the boat.

The trip is as much fun as it was the year before. I still don't have a camera with a zoom lens, so don't bother taking pictures even as the whales surface all around us, almost close enough at times to touch. They seem to be seeking us out and to be cavorting solely for our pleasure. Or maybe they are just enjoying being alive. Their graceful black bodies arc out of the water, and then plunge below the surface. Sometimes they swim under the boat and, as though to surprise us, surface on the other side. Some of their splashes reach into the boat.

Ken's microphone picks up some of their singing. The passengers ooh and aah in delight. Then the whales are gone as quickly as they came.

When they're gone, I feel, simultaneously, blessed by their presence and bereft by their departure—a bit like good human relationships. They all must end sometime. The secret is to fully enjoy them while we have them so that, even in our grief at our loss, we know we have been blessed.

On the way back Ken hugs the coast and ducks into Bear Cove, delighting some kids who are playing on the shore. I can pick out more landmarks this summer than last, but still can't see my cabin, though I can tell where it is from the opening in the trees where I sat this morning.

That night over dinner Jim and Derek suggest that we all go down to Ingonish for a few days. Then they'll go on to Halifax on Sunday, stay overnight there, and be ready to catch their plane early Monday morning. I like the plan. I'm in no hurry to say good-bye, and it will be fun to share some of the sights on that side of the island with them.

*

* *

We decide to start our trip to Ingonish with a hike out to Money Point Light. On the way we stop at the phone to call the Ingonish Beach campground and make reservations for two nights. Yes, dogs are permitted, fortunately, since Amber, having been left the day before, made sure she came along today. We leave my car in the tiny hamlet known as St. Margaret's Village, taking the rental car up the small, winding, unpaved road toward Money Point. At one place the road climbs up a mountain, and we pull over and get out to admire the spectacular view. To the east the Atlantic Ocean spreads before us, seemingly without limit. To the south we can see the long, curving, sandy beach where John Cabot supposedly landed in 1497, and, on the other side, the rocky headlands of White Point. To the north we can see part of Money Point and, to the west, the St. Lawrence Bay and the protected harbor where Ken keeps his boat.

We continue to the point where the trail to the lighthouse starts, park the car, grab our day pack with our lunch and Amber's leash and let her out of the car. The trail is a nice, gentle, downhill walk to the light. First we are in the woods, but soon we are out on the headland and walking along the top of the rocky bluff. It is windy and a little cool, so I am glad I brought my scarf. The sun is receding behind a bank of clouds that threaten to blanket the sky. Ahead of us we can see the waves breaking on the irregular rocks of the point and the e-shaped coves into which the point has been shaped by the wind and waves. It is a wild, desolate place.

"Imagine living out here," I muse, thinking that it is not hard to understand why the light at the point is now electronic and unmanned. On the other hand, living out here would certainly have its own appeal.

"I like the space and the isolation," says Derek. "It reminds me a little bit of home. The ocean is even a little like the prairie, except for the waves. They're awesome. Maybe because I never saw the ocean until I was an adult, I am always struck by God's power when I am in a place like this." I share Derek's sense of awe and am more than a little startled to hear him express what I so often feel in watching the ocean's waves break on some unyielding rocky promontory, but have never expressed to anyone. Even though I often feel close to God when I am out in nature, I am most aware of His power when I see waves crashing on rocky shores.

We find a boulder to shelter us somewhat from the wind without blocking our view of the ocean. We eat in silence, partly because we are all fascinated by the scene and partly because the waves and wind tend to drown out our voices. Amber keeps shaking her head as though that will get rid of the wind. We poke around a little after lunch, but find that the rocks very quickly become impassible in every direction. Even Jim can only go so far and then has to return. We linger on our way back to the car, all the more so because it is uphill. Mostly, though, we hate to leave this bleakly beautiful scene.

We stop at Cabot's Landing and take the byroads out to Dingwall and White Point on our way to Ingonish. We take another short hike up Sugarloaf Mountain. By the time we reach the campground, dusk is starting to fall. I realize that the long summer nights are getting shorter. We fix supper and play scrabble by the light of the lantern.

Amber, of course, thinks that she is an old hand at camping by now. Still, the presence of so many other people and dogs is unnerving to her, and we keep her on her leash. She lies at our feet contentedly enough, but keeps a watchful eye on who is walking by. Periodically she raises her head and ears and sniffs. Sometimes we even hear a low growl deep in her throat or, if someone comes too close, she gets up and makes sure they do not enter our space. More and more I realize what a good watchdog and companion she must have been for Sadie's aunt. Sadie told me that Marion is going to have to be moved to a nursing home and probably won't be able to take Amber with her. She'd asked me if I would want to keep Amber in that case and I'd told her I'd think about it.

The next morning we all hike out to the end of Middle Head Peninsula. The view from there is similar to the view John and I had from the tall ship we'd taken an evening sail on the year before. It is an easy, enjoyable hike. Amber is happy to be unleashed and literally runs circles around us. Derek starts talking about some of his favorite horseback rides back home, and I find myself hoping I can visit there sometime and go on some of those rides myself.

On the way back, as we walk past the imposing and luxurious Keltic Lodge, Derek tells me that he and Jim have made reservations for dinner there to celebrate my birthday. They'd already checked, and informal attire is fine. I'm touched by their thoughtfulness. I had wanted to eat there last year, but we hadn't had the time. The food is supposed to be excellent, and we can tell from here that the views will also be magnificent. It's a long time since I have eaten anywhere fancier than the Rusty Anchor.

After lunch, the "kids"—Jim, Derek and Amber—go off to hike up Franey Mountain. I doze over my book and finally just give up and take a nap and then a shower. I put together the most elegant attire I have with me for the occasion (my "good" jeans, a turtleneck and a scarf), fix a cup of tea and read while Jim and Derek get ready. We leave Amber leashed to a tree, looking after us with reproach in her eyes. I can't help but remember how John used to tease my whole family when we were dating and someone would talk about the expression in our dog's eyes. Jim has not heard that bit of family lore, but can imagine his father's tone, mocking but affectionate, as he twitted us for our anthropomorphism. That leads to other humorous family anecdotes from both families. By the time we reach the Lodge, we are in the mood for a festive evening.

And a festive dinner it is. We are seated at a window in the Purple Thistle Room, and the changing light over Ingonish and the bay between us is a suitable backdrop for our good spirits. We are all feeling very pleased with ourselves. I'm pleased to see Jim so happy, pleased with Derek, pleased that they came to seek my advice and to include me as part of an important vacation. They are pleased with each other, with my reactions, with the locale and with my good spirits. We toast each other, share tastes of each other's dinners, approve everything, splurge on dessert, which we justify by all the hiking we have done, and recount innumerable funny stories to each other. Jim has some customer stories that practically have us thrown out for disrupting the restaurant as we laugh until our sides hurt.

"Those are pretty funny stories, Jim, but I'd take customers any day over professors who regard their doctoral students as pawns in a larger game," Derek reflects as our laughter subsides.

"It sounds as though you have a story to tell about an example," I interject.

"Well, it's not as funny as Jim's stories, though it does have its humorous side." He glances at Jim, who obviously has already heard the tale.

"You mean the story about how one of your professors tried to have you throw out your dissertation because he was feuding with the chair of your committee?" Jim asks wryly.

I turn to Derek, "Really?"

"Yes, yes, it's all quite true," he said. "After I'd already accepted the job at American University. It cost me a lot of time and worry, not to mention sleep."

Though his face wears a shy grin, the trace of irony I detect in Derek's voice captures my attention. I am reminded of when I was typing John's dissertation for him. Things can get pretty tense when you have a deadline and unexpected obstacles loom.

"So, what happened?" I ask, my interest piqued.

"Well," Derek shrugs. "Everything came to a head when he sent out this really scathing memo to all tenured faculty members in the department saying it was a disgrace that this work was allowed to be done by a University of Wisconsin graduate student in its distinguished history department. He went on to say that if my dissertation proceeded as planned, it would cheapen the department and lessen the respect of everyone on the faculty. The whole thing became a big *cause célèbre*." Derek pauses momentarily. The grin on his face has broadened a bit, and he glances from Jim to me. "Needless to say, this was not what I needed."

"So, what did you do?"

Jim interrupts, gleefully, "He simply gave his nemesis a very large dose of his own medicine!"

Puzzled, I look at Derek for illumination.

"In a way I guess I did," he admits, with a slight laugh. "I just applied his attack on me to his own work, and sent out a memo of mock woe to everyone he'd sent his memo to, saying, in effect, that if I were to give up comparing minority groups on the basis of his criticism, no one would be able to compare anything—including him." The note of irony in his voice has changed to one of satisfaction. He's almost beaming. Jim smiles at Derek with obvious pride.

"I guess it worked, based on your current job," I observe.

"Yes, it did," he modestly replies. "I sent the memo around on Friday and by Monday it was clear that it had had the desired effect of giving everyone—even the offending professor, much to my surprise and relief—a good laugh, defusing the issue and allowing me to finish my dissertation on time. And, I must say, in appreciation of my nemesis, the whole thing did make me much more sensitive to the large and inherent differences among the groups I study, as well as to their similarities."

As he finishes his story, I realize anew that this man I am thinking of more and more as my future son-in-law is a good match for Jim. Like him, Derek is a person of depth who wears well.

I am so engrossed in Derek's story that I do not notice a small band setting up behind me. Therefore, I am taken completely by surprise when the first sounds of mellow dance music float across the room. The song is "Misty," and the music eminently danceable.

Suddenly I am transported back in time to our favorite fancy neighborhood restaurant one New Year's Eve, and John and I are dancing to the strains of "Misty," played well by a special trio brought in for the evening. We loved dancing and did it all too rarely. But that night the manager moved the tables aside so we all could dance. And we danced long beyond the time we thought we would leave. We danced fast dances and slow dances. We improvised and two-stepped and had eyes only for each other.

And, after we'd scurried home in the cold, clear night air, we continued dancing. Until we started scattering clothes around the living room. And wound up in the bedroom, caught up in passion. And I wondered how, in loving each other, after all these years, we continually surprised and delighted ourselves and felt a newness in the act of love even as our deep knowledge of each other contributed to our ease and mutual pleasure. I've avoided thinking about how much I would miss that until this moment. I feel a shudder begin deep in my soul and spread through my whole body. My body is racked with sobs, and I lean on the table, abandoning all sense of everything but my loss.

Although I don't hear Jim getting up and coming over to me, I feel his arms around me, and hear him trying to comfort me as though I were the child and he the parent. "It's all right, Mom. It's going to be all right."

In the middle of my grief, anger flares. "Oh, how can you say that?! You don't understand! I'll never feel John's body close to mine, never experience his touch again, never be able to stroke his beard, his hands . . ." My voice trails off as I mentally complete the sentence, but can't bring myself to speak my thoughts. I lift my tear-stained face to look at him, anger draining out of me as quickly as it arose. As I look at my son, I see in his eyes a deep empathy and understanding even before he speaks. In a flash of comprehension, I realize that his own struggles with himself, with me and with society because of his sexual orientation are the source of his ability to feel my pain.

"Oh, Mom," he says softly and with immense compassion. "I *do* understand."

With his words a sense of relief and peace sweep over me. I can almost hear the last vestiges of the barriers I've built around myself since John's death crumble. By sharing the last, and most deeply hidden, part of my loss, I know that I am taking a gigantic step toward healing. I take a deep breath and look around me. Derek is watching Jim's face intently. The band has stopped and other diners are staring at us with unabashed curiosity. A bit sheepishly, I smile at them. Norwegian that I am, it is not like me to be part of an emotional scene. Under the circumstances, however, I do not feel the least bit repentant.

Not trusting my voice yet, I squeeze Jim's hand and repair to the luxurious ladies' room. The cold water I splash over my face feels wonderful.

"Well," Jim says as I return and the band strikes up another danceable tune, "would it help or hurt to dance?" Jim has seen his parents dance, and knows how much it meant to me.

I make a face. "Maybe it's like getting back up on a horse after you've been thrown. Unless I plan to live the rest of my life avoiding music and dancing, I guess I might as well start now. And you're the perfect partner for my reentry." Jim combines John's musical ability with my love of dancing and is one of the few people other than John with whom I feel comfortable on the dance floor. He is a superb dancer and leads even more effortlessly than John did. Somewhat to my surprise, I enjoy being out there with him.

Then Derek invites me to dance, and that's fine. Then the two of them dance. They look great together and are the best dancers on the floor. People, both on the floor and off, do a bit of a double take at seeing two men dancing together. I guess that it is not a frequent event up here, if, indeed, it has ever happened before. But they look so at ease and cover the floor with such grace and style that after a while the slight suspicion on people's faces turns to simple admiration. They are a treat to watch.

The three of us enjoy the dancing more than I could ever have believed and stay until the band packs up. By the time I get back to the campsite and crawl into my tent with Amber, I am emotionally and physically exhausted. But, it is a good, clean kind of exhaustion, and I sleep more soundly than I have in months.

Chapter 20

Good-byes

The next morning is cloudy again and drizzly. In spite of the weather, I feel joy in my heart and find myself singing as I start pancakes for breakfast. I know that something changed last night. I no longer feel dragged down by haunting memories of the past. For the first time since that horrible April morning, I want to go to church and praise God in the presence of others.

My mood is catching. Jim and Derek are happy to come along. We leave Amber to guard the campsite. She looks a little anxious as we drive off, but doesn't bark or try to follow us, so we figure she trusts us to return.

Although we choose the church for its proximity and convenient hour of worship, I feel at home as soon as we enter. It is a simple wooden church with clear glass windows looking out over trees and woods in the background. The greeters are warm without being intrusive and the organ is playing familiar hymns of praise. It has a Presbyterian feel to it.

The text for the day is Mark 9:38-40. This is the passage in which one of the disciples tells Jesus that he had seen a man casting out demons in Jesus' name and had told him to stop because he was not one of their group. Jesus overturns this attempt to draw a line in a tight circle around "us" and to exclude "them." He dramatically expands the circle of who is "us," with the simple statement, "Whoever is not against us is for us." The preacher, a young man who speaks with simple humility and power, asks how this lesson applies to us in a world where communities are increasingly diverse religiously, politically and ideologically. Most people live surrounded by others who are "not following us." We are tempted to do what the disciple did, to draw lines to distinguish "us" from "them." We can see the fruits of that in Kosovo, in Africa, in the Middle East, in Ireland, and even in Canada.

The preacher poses the dilemma of how we maintain our treasured beliefs, values and traditions and still achieve our desire for fellowship, community, active conversation and peace with people who do not share our beliefs. Now he has my full attention. This is a problem I know. He is very clear that we cannot resolve this dilemma successfully by trying to get everyone to agree with us. Nor can we do it by avoiding talking about our beliefs. Instead, if we are firmly rooted in our faith, we will be able to listen to someone who is in a different place describe the source of their strength and their beliefs without being threatened by them. Hmm. That seems to imply that when I get emotional about something with which I disagree, the reason I get so emotional is that I am not yet sure of my own beliefs. That is a big enough thought that I tuck it away for future reference.

When I tune in again, the sermon is ending with a reference to clergy important in early Canadian history. One was a French Catholic priest and the other a Scottish Presbyterian minister. They worked and met in a time when Catholics and Protestants were still exiling, imprisoning and even making martyrs of each other. Yet the priest welcomed the minister as a "beloved brother." The two saw each other often in the years to come and worked together to achieve common goals in the wilderness. We know of the relationship through the words of a diary kept by the minister. The preacher reads one short entry from that diary of long ago:

> Priest GR calls on me at my lodging. We had a free and pleasant conversation. He says there is much work for me to do and wished me success. He stays to tea. I request him to ask a blessing. He answers that he is not accustomed to our mode, that he performs such service in the Latin and if acceptable he will do it that way.

The music swells and we all get to our feet to sing, "Join Christians, Rise to Sing." The "alleluias" from the chorus of that song ring in my head as we walk out of church and drive back to the campground. Jim and Derek enjoyed the sermon, too, and Derek, in fact, is able to fill in some of the historical context. The treatment of minorities through history has been a fascination of his since he was in high school. As we drive back to the campground, he gives us examples of other gracious acts and friendships across painful divides during different eras of conflict and repression.

After greeting Amber and being lavishly welcomed back by her, we pack up. None of us is hungry enough to be inspired by our meager remaining store of rations. I tell them about the Bell Buoy Restaurant John and I found in Baddeck, which is on their way back to Halifax. While we have the map out, I show them the campground where John and I camped near the airport. To my pleased surprise, I note I do not feel quite the same sense of loss when I mention John that I did before my emotional scene the night before.

"I'm not sure when I'll be back," I tell them. "Sometime before Tor comes in September. I'll let you know."

"Let us know if you want company the first night—or anytime, for that matter. And, you know, if you decide to keep Amber, I'll be glad to put her up whenever you want to go out of town. My dog is always happy to have another dog around to improve the dog/cat ratio!"

"Thanks, Derek. I appreciate both offers."

With hugs and waves, they are off. Although I feel a pang of sadness to see them go, mostly I'm grateful for the visit and that they'll be in D.C. when I do decide to return.

Amber needs a walk before cooping her up in the car for our trip back. And I need some time to think before concentrating on driving. We walk out to the beach. It is still cloudy, dreary, cool and drizzling off and on, and the beach is deserted. We walk along until I find a boulder to perch on while Amber, free of her leash, chases waves, pokes at strange, smelly objects, chases birds and just generally enjoys being a dog.

I replay the sermon from that morning in my mind, focusing on the parts that most moved me. Questions of how and when to talk to Stephanie and Sonia about Jim and Derek have been lurking at the back of my mind during the last few days. The sermon brought them to the surface. I know that Greta's reaction will be much like mine. She will want to meet Derek, of course, and get to know him if he is going to become a member of the family. Even before that, though, she will be excited and happy for Jim and thrilled at the idea of a commitment ceremony. If possible, I know she will want to be there. Rolf, too, and his family will be happy to hear the news. I imagine him explaining the ceremony to his kids in his calm, matter-of-fact way.

Sonia's and Stephanie's reactions are likely to be more complicated and harder to predict. Then, too, each of them will have to deal with the question of how and when to talk to their children about this new relationship. I think that Sonia has probably talked to at least her two oldest sons about the fact that their Uncle Jim is gay, but I do not know what she told them or what their reactions were. I doubt if Stephanie has talked about Jim's being gay to any of her children, who are, of course, younger. In both cases, the kids are more likely to hear negative things than positive about homosexuals and homosexuality in their churches and among their friends.

The sermon helps me think differently about their reactions than I might have otherwise. I pray silently for wisdom and God's guidance. I know that Sonia prays for God's will to be done in Jim's life, and I repeat that prayer for him and for all of us, including Derek. I pray that all of us will be open to God's voice and willing to let go of anything in us that does not come from Him. I pray I am able to know when and how to talk to Sonia and Stephanie about Jim and Derek. I pray I will be able to do so with respect both for Jim and Derek and their relationship, and for Sonia and Stephanie and their reactions. I pray for God's will to be done in Tor's life and for Tor to be open to the possibilities God has in mind for him.

I acknowledge my own weaknesses. I recognize that I sometimes pelt Stephanie, especially, with writings that support my views in an attempt to persuade her of the rightness of my conclusions. I pray that God helps me to let go of that desire and be willing to be a channel of His peace and to listen to His truth, wherever that might lead me. I pray that I am able to love as He would have me love.

Reversing my usual order of prayer, I end with a heart overflowing with gratitude and thanks for all the blessings God has given me: for Stephanie and all the blessings that have flowed from her and from our reunion; for her adoptive parents and all that they have done for her; for Sonia and her loving heart; for the ways in which both Sonia and Stephanie exemplify lives open to God's glory and presence and for their God-centered homes and families.

I thank God for Tor, for Greta, for Jim and for Derek and for the trust and love they have all shared with me. I thank God for the healing I have experienced over and over again in myself, in my relationships and in every branch of my family, including Rolf and his family. I thank God for the relationship I was privileged to have with John and for the healing He has brought about within me this summer. I thank Him for surrounding me with love, family and friends so that I can, once again, feel cradled in His love at a time of need.

And then I feel peace and know that it is time to go home.

Epilogue

On the long drive home, I feel amazingly light-hearted and eager to return to a life which had seemed as dry and lifeless as sawdust as I headed the other direction a few scant months ago. Truly, I have experienced salvation. And, although I retreated from people when I fled north, nothing would have changed without the love of people I am blessed to call family.

My memories of my father, the first gift this sojourn gave me, helped me achieve perspective in the midst of my pain. Those recollections put me in touch with the source of passion in my life. My zeal and ardor for justice were the fuel I needed to move beyond the torpor which characterized me when I first arrived.

Greta not only pampered me, she also made me realize that, like Mother, I have the spirit and resilience it takes to seek redemption in my darkest hour. And, of course, Jim—and Derek. Without them, I wouldn't be so joyous now. By coming to me for advice and wisdom, Jim drew me out of my preoccupation with my grief at the exact moment I was ready. Surely the timing was arranged by God! Maybe it was the diversion that opened me up to the last wellsprings of debilitating grief within me. Jim's presence, empathy and understanding when I finally experienced them made me able to let go. Could I have done this without him? I doubt it. I thank God again for His infinite wisdom and mercy. How could I have doubted His compassion?

As Amber stirs in her sleep and I glance over at her stretched out on the passenger seat, I realize that even she played a role, as did siblings, children and grandchildren who surrounded me with their abundant love even when we were not together.

Amber and I arrive in D.C. early on a Monday afternoon. I introduce her to the building and to our building manager. She loves all the new smells and seems at home in what I still think of as "our" apartment. My apprehensions about introducing an animal into an apartment designed for the "post-kid, post-cat" phase of our lives vanish when I see how much at home she looks. The Oriental carpets show off her amber-colored fur to great advantage. She loses no time in getting a good olfactory sense of the entire apartment. Finally, ready to settle down, she chooses a spot where she can watch the door and also be close to me as I sit in my chair sorting through the mounds of mail waiting for me.

Having Amber with me makes it easier to return to the building with so many memories of John, including the painful memories of our last morning together, ending so dramatically with his collapse. My memory of the events after that is a confusing blur of sirens, riding to the hospital in the ambulance, the fading hope he would be all right, the rising panic when I knew he would not and the overwhelming grief. I know those memories will remain with me.

At the same time I realize the summer has changed me. When I left, I wasn't sure I could—or even wanted to—go on with my life. Now, although I miss John, and know I always will, I am ready, even eager, to go back to church and to get together with my friends. I know there are decisions ahead of me. A new stage of life is in front of me. Now I know I will want to immerse myself in something that will help change the world, or at least my small corner of it, for the better. When I left, I couldn't imagine doing that.

What has made the difference? Time certainly played a part, but wasn't enough by itself. Amber? No, she's a great companion, but would only have deepened my sorrow if nothing else had happened. The good wishes and sympathy of family and friends? Certainly this, too, was important. Greta's visit and nurturing was wonderful and started me on the road to recovery. Even that, however, can't explain where I am today.

Today, I am actually looking forward to the future. I have regained my love of life, as well as my desire to live. Today I know I am a complete person without John. Now I am happy to be who I am and where I am.

I owe that to Jim and Derek. They came to me because they wanted something which only I could give: the perspective, love and yes, even wisdom, of a loving mother. By responding to that need, and by becoming a part of an important time in their lives, I was rescued from my own self-absorption and misery. I feel free and grateful to them and to God.

With a surprisingly light heart, I decide the unpacking and reentry duties can wait, and call Annabelle, my walking companion and neighbor. Yes, she is free for a walk and, of course, she would love to meet Amber. I have a lot to tell her and a lot to hear. I'm back.

This book was composed in Palatino and designed by
Brown Composition Systems, Inc., Bloomington, Indiana.

Cover design by Melisa Pool.
Front cover illustration by David R. Dudley.
Back cover photograph by Suly Rebori Uberman.

Produced by Gary Pool.